Life by Pumpkin

Book 1

A Cat's View on Everything

Life by Pumpkin

Book 1

A Cat's View on Everything

Leslie Popp

First paperback edition May 2023

Book design by Leslie Popp

ISBN: 979-8-9881025-0-2

In loving memory of Pumpkin, who will always be my little boy. His affection and heartwarming antics colored my days and left me with fond memories that always make me smile. The following stories recount actual events from Pumpkin's point of view. I hope they bring you joy as well.

- Leslie

Table of Contents

Breaking Out of Jail

It all started when I was in jail. I'm not sure what my crime was, but they stuck me in a cell with only a standard-issue towel to nap on, second-rate food that was not my normal brand, and a box full of sand. I could see rows of other cells, stacked two or three high, from my view between the bars. Their occupants gazed at me with curiosity. It was noisy, and I spent most of my day lounging and contemplating what would come next in life. Would I ever get to run free again? In the darkest times, I paced from side to side, counting my steps, or pressed my head against the cold bars and watched my cellmates go about their daily routines, wondering how we ended up here.

Once or twice a day, someone would open the door, provide fresh food and water, and sift the sandbox like they were looking for buried treasure. This was the best part of my day, and I made sure to act especially cute and gently nuzzle their hands so they would pet me. When the visitor paused their duties to stroke my head and back, I purred loudly and would drift off to sleep, forgetting where I was for a while. Eventually, the visitor would leave, and I would sigh heavily and go back to staring out between the bars.

One day, I was minding my own business, not expecting it to be different from any other day, and wishing I could escape to the top of the nearby cells to get a better view, when an unfamiliar female approached my cell. She whispered something, opened the door, and crouched down to peer in at me. I blinked a bit nervously and was drawn to her face, which seemed kind and welcoming. I rose from the towel, where I was curled up, and she reached out slowly so I could sniff her hand. Gently, she rubbed the top of my head, and I advanced to the edge of my cell to get a closer look at her face.

I sat motionless as she continued to caress my cheeks, the itchy spot behind my ears, and my back. I instinctively purred and settled down in front of her to bask in the attention. She didn't seem to be in a hurry and remained totally focused on me. For a moment, I forgot where I was and imagined being somewhere quieter, with just the two of us enjoying each other's company.

Suddenly, she shifted from side to side, glanced around, and withdrew her hand. I was worried she was about to leave and felt my heart sink.

"Oh, please don't go!" I thought desperately.

But instead of retreating, she repositioned herself on the edge of my cell and managed to scoot inside my cramped enclosure. I hesitated until she resumed rhythmically petting me from head to tail, then gingerly placed my front paws onto her leg and stretched my face up to hers. She didn't pull back, but instead leaned in toward me. Our foreheads touched for a blissful moment,

2

and she held perfectly still while I sniffed her nose, hair, and then nose again. Feeling more confident, I rubbed my cheek against hers and was rewarded with a light hug. She was warm and soft, and I could feel my heart swell with emotion.

Growing bolder, I climbed onto her lap, and she wrapped both arms around me, holding me to her chest. She was so gentle, and that made me want to snuggle. I could hear her heart beating, and it calmed my nerves. What if she didn't like me? What if she wasn't the nice lady she seemed to be? I was prepared to take that risk.

She spoke in a low tone, and I committed the sound of her voice to memory, so I would always recognize it, even if my eyes were closed. Turning in a tight circle, I settled onto her lap, and she began the soothing petting again, continuing to talk to me, although I didn't know what she was saying. I was so at ease that I soon drifted off for an afternoon nap.

Suddenly, my ears perked up, and I realized another woman was standing nearby. The two of them were speaking, and I turned from one to the other, wondering if they were talking about me. I heard my name, Pumpkin, repeated a few times, and I felt something warm and fuzzy well up inside of me.

This went on for a while, and I was loving every minute of it. I hoped it would never end. But alas, it had to. After she left, I spent a long time thinking about our afternoon together. I was trying to burn the image of her face and the way she smelled into my memory, so I would never forget our special moment. I didn't expect to ever see her again.

But to my surprise, a few days later, she was at my door. I couldn't believe it, and I immediately got to my feet to welcome her into my cell. I eagerly strolled over, and she again positioned herself just inside the door. I began rubbing against her arm and hand and crawled onto her lap for much-needed hugs and snuggles. She held me to her chest, and I nuzzled at her chin, breathing in her increasingly familiar scent.

I wanted to adopt her, so we could be together forever. I would make space in my cell if she wanted to move in. I'm sure we could figure it out. I'm not good at sharing, but I would learn if it meant I could keep her.

Then something scary and exciting happened. She brought over a small, portable room with a new, soft towel neatly folded on the bottom, and she slowly coaxed me into it. I didn't know what was happening, but I had the sense that she wanted to take me somewhere. Trusting my instincts, I climbed in and settled onto the towel. I peeked out through the holes in the side of the room as I was carried through the jail and into a sunny room that seemed vaguely familiar. After a brief pause, we continued out of the building, and for the first time in a year, I could feel fresh air on my whiskers. It was quieter out here, and I couldn't smell the other cats.

I closed my eyes and enjoyed the sway of the room as we continued on our journey. I could see the sun shining and hear nearby chirps coming from the trees.

The woman kept talking encouragingly, and I told myself to be brave. She had broken me out of jail, and that had to count for something.

After a brief ride in a much larger box that moved, jerked, and made a humming noise, the woman carried me into a new building. She set my bedroom on the ground and opened the door, sitting a few feet away and softly calling my name.

I'll admit, I was terrified. I didn't know what dangers might lurk just outside this small space or if there were other cats or beasts here that might be cruel to me, but I didn't have a choice. I had come this far, and I had to go explore this new location. I really wanted her to hold me again, and she wouldn't be able to do that if I cowered in here forever.

Cautiously, I emerged and scanned the area. There were no signs of movement outside of the two women. I trotted over to the one that had been in my cell, and she tenderly ran her hand over the top of my head. I remained close to her for a moment until I decided nothing was waiting to pounce. Then I began to give in to my growing curiosity.

The floor was soft and squishy, a nice change from the metal floor of my cell. It was like having fluffy towels everywhere. I began to wander about, sniffing everything in sight and peering in every nook and cranny, cataloging my new surroundings. I peeked nervously around doorways before entering a new room and marveled at the amount of open space. It would take some getting used to after my long confinement. I was finally free to wander and didn't know where to explore first.

I crawled under the bed, deciding that it would make a great hiding spot for me in the future, and then continued exploring the area. There were a lot of tall ledges where I could perch, but I decided to evaluate those later. Best not to rush through the assessment of what appears to be my new territory.

The women followed me from a distance, and I liked having them in sight in case of danger. I discovered bowls filled with food and water and helped myself to a snack after careful inspection. I hoped whoever it belonged to didn't get angry, but it was so tasty that I ate all of it. In another room, I noticed a covered sandbox, and I stuck my head inside to investigate. To my delight, it was clean and didn't smell like another cat had ever been in there. I hopped in and marked it as mine just in case anyone else wanted to claim it while my back was turned.

I wandered back to the women, and they fawned over me to my heart's content. They showed me a tall ledge sitting atop a pole covered in soft fabric, and I immediately loved it. It was all mine! I quickly scaled the tower, feeling proud of my athletic abilities, and surveyed the territory below.

They introduced me to a fuzzy mouse and a fish with feathers for a tail, as well as several other characters that were scattered about the room. I couldn't believe how wonderful everything was here. It was like a dream, and I hoped to make this place my permanent address.

Sheer exhaustion began to make my eyelids droop, and my feet felt heavy. With all of the commotion and excitement, I had missed my afternoon nap, which was generally unheard of. The woman from my cell was sitting on the couch, and I hopped up next to her, reassured by her welcoming gesture. I curled up on her lap, as I had done before, and she held me while I fell into a deep, happy sleep. I decided that this was my new home, and I was going to adopt her.

God Among Men

-Five Years Later-

I am a god among men, master of my domain, and ruler of the free world! I reign over every inch of this apartment, and my army of loyal mouse toys is at my disposal. I leave no corner unexplored, no box unturned, and no high ledge unexamined, no matter the potential danger. I nap whenever and wherever I please, but mostly I prefer fuzzy blankets, the sunny spot by the window, or the cradle of my climbing tower, with my blue and white fish toy tucked under my chin.

I diligently patrol the perimeter of my domain every night before bed, sniffing around the doors, looking out all the windows, checking for any security risks, and making sure my food and water are still there. Yep, they're still there this evening! I can hardly wait for breakfast when, without fail, there will be another offering of my favorite wet food. The dry kibble poured into my bowl as an overnight snack is deserving of a scathing review, but I'm unsure where to send the complaint.

As it approaches midnight, everything seems to be in order, and the apartment is quiet. My mom is already in bed, and I can hear her breathing slowly and steadily in the next room. Silently, I stroll over to the bedroom

8

door and nudge it open with my head, squeezing through the narrow opening before it closes behind me. The room is dark, and a gentle breeze and a noisy hum are coming from the gray box that is stuck in the window. The movement of the air ruffles the hanging fabric that keeps the room shrouded in darkness even after the sun comes up.

I sit beside the bed with my feet together and my tail wrapped around me, the end flicking slightly. I gaze contentedly at Mom as she lies there so peacefully on her small section of my bed. She says that I have my own pillow, but really all the pillows are mine, and both sides are mine too.

Quietly, I spring up onto one of the wooden storage boxes that are situated on either side of the bed, landing with my feet straddling the odd, glowing rectangle that she is always carrying around and sometimes annoyingly talking into. I sniff at the coffee cup placed purposefully on the corner of the wooden box. It's filled to the brim with water and should just be called a water cup; in fact, it should be called my water cup. After all, I don't drink coffee. Deciding it's fresh and acceptable, I daintily begin to lap up the cool water, my tiny, pink tongue darting out quickly to spoon it into my mouth without wasting a drop.

When I've had my fill, I wander over to the bed and step gingerly onto my soft, fluffy blankie. Treading directly across the pillow and bounding over Mom's head, I circle around to her left side, feeling her stir from the disturbance. I can't believe she goes to bed before I'm ready and isn't already sleeping in the perfect snuggle position.

She whispers something quietly to me. Probably, "Oh, you're the smartest and most handsome cat ever, and I adore every inch of you," or something to that effect.

She then smooths out the blanket and moves one arm out to the side, like I've trained her to do. This training took persistence, but over a few weeks and with a good rewards system in place, she learned to position herself in a specific way so I can snuggle next to her.

Stepping over her arm, I tuck myself against her left side. Always the left, not the right; I'm very particular. Resting my head on her shoulder, stretching one paw out over her chest, and plastering my body against hers, I let her engulf me in a warm embrace so her steady heartbeat can lull me to sleep. She kisses the top of my head, and I start to purr almost involuntarily as I drift off into dreams of mighty mountains made of tuna cans.

Midnight Scuffles

My ear twitches, picking up some distant sound. Perhaps it's those humans I watch in the apartment windows across the courtyard. Or maybe it's a mouse! I'm on high alert and scan the room for intruders of the four-legged, furry variety. Hmm, no movement detected.

I stride across Mom in her sleep, and she makes a soft grunting noise. Hopping to the ground, I listen intently before slipping out into the hallway, peering into the bathroom, and checking my food again. Yep, the food is still here, and the coast is clear.

Everything is dark, even though it's almost morning, and by that, I mean the sun will be up in three hours, which is practically morning. Stealthily, I trot into the adjacent room, spring up to the back of the couch, and check the window. The perimeter seems secure, and there are no lights on in the other apartments that suggest an imminent threat. Humans are sluggish and sleep late, not like me. I am superior in every way, almost ethereal.

Suddenly, I spot a familiar form lying under the table where Mom eats her meals. Even in the dark, I know that shape. How dare he intrude upon my domain! With a surge of energy, I launch myself from the couch, scamper under the table, and pounce on the unsuspecting

11

mouse, sinking my sharp teeth into his purple fur. With his tail dangling from my mighty jaws, I sprint into the hallway and toss him high into the air. He lands with a soft thud, and I leap forward, smacking him hard with my paw before he has a chance to run again. He goes spinning and sliding across the wood floor, and I follow in hot pursuit. I run a circle around him to create confusion, so he doesn't know which way to go. Then I retreat behind my climbing tower and crouch, tail flicking, eyes wide, waiting for his next move.

He lies still. I can't tell if he's breathing, but it could be a clever deception. I remain motionless, hoping that he'll assume I've given up. Seconds tick by, and I grow anxious. I race over, snatch him up again, and bound up onto my cat tower, where I skillfully pin him between my front paws and scratch at him with my back claws. He doesn't make a sound, but to my satisfaction, a few pieces of fur go flying. For good measure, I gnaw on his tail and then fling him from the tower to the cold, hard floor below.

As I watch him fly through the air, all I can think is, "Oh no you don't, there's no escaping from me today!"

With adrenaline pulsing through my veins, I sprint after him. My feet slide on the slippery floor, and I overshoot my target, skidding within inches of his matted, furry frame. I turn on a dime and blindside him with another powerful slap. He sails across the room, hitting the wall behind my food bowl. I am right on his heels and come to a halt about a foot away. I take a knee, crouch low, and watch the intruder for signs of life. No movement. I won this round, but you can never be too sure; it's best to stay on guard for a bit.

Suddenly, my nose detects a familiar aroma. Hmm, turkey and rice, if I'm not mistaken. I contemplate my food bowl for a moment, but this is no time for food. I'm on a mission to put down the pesky mouse scout so he doesn't report back to the opposing army, which is no doubt assembled nearby. Wait, do I smell a bit of chicken broth mixed in? Maybe I should have a snack while I await my opponent's next move. They do say an army marches on its stomach or something like that, right? Besides, what if his comrades invade while I'm sleeping and eat all my food? I can't let that happen. It's mine! All mine!

Feeling suddenly ravenous, I gobble up my food, savoring the turkey flavor and crunching loudly on the kibble. They can't have it if it's in my stomach. When my bowl is empty, I sit back and assess my work, satisfied with my accomplishments. The intruder has been neutralized, and my belly is full. As my very manly red and black bowl says, "Good Cat."

I retreat to the bedroom for a cat nap before breakfast.

Training My Human

I believe my morning awakening should commence with the song from *The Lion King*. You know the one when Mufasa holds Simba up to all the other animals and says that everything the light touches belongs to him. This ritual makes perfect sense to me. I also rule over everything the light touches and everything it doesn't touch. The humans and the hordes of mice and fish toys are all my subjects.

I yawn, displaying my teeth like the little lion I am. Then I move on to my morning yoga routine, stretching my front and back paws out as far as they can go and arching my back so I reach my full length. Finally, I roll to my feet, feeling ready to take on the day. The faintest hint of sunlight, almost imperceptible, is now visible, and I decide that it's time for Mom to get up and feed me.

I stroll casually across her pillow, her head shifting slightly with the movement. Then I circle back and walk across her chest. She stirs abruptly, and her eyes flutter open. I move in close and sniff her forehead, making sure my whiskers tickle her face so she doesn't go back to sleep.

She reaches up to scratch the top of my head and whispers, "Good morning."

I love when she pets me like this. She knows just where the itchy spots are by my eyebrows and behind my ears. I lean in and close my eyes, enjoying the peaceful moment.

She reaches for that glowing, rectangular thing on the bedside storage box, and it suddenly lights up, as if on command, catching her attention. I knew I should have knocked it to the ground last night and pushed it under the bed, where she wouldn't be able to find it so easily. I don't like being bested by a lighted box. I place my two front paws on her chest and position my head in front of it, so she has to stare into my eyes and ignore all other distractions. She pauses a moment, and I take the opportunity to rub my face against her hands, forcing her to lower the glowing object and pat me lightly. I let out a satisfied purr. This is part of the positive reinforcement rewards system I was telling you about earlier. I turn and bring my face right up to hers, lightly touching our noses together. She smiles and hugs me, murmuring softly. I assume it must be something about how I am the cutest little boy ever. Even though it is totally obvious and true, I still like hearing it several times a day.

Now comes the tricky part of getting her out of bed for breakfast. I begin to pace back and forth, walking in circles over her, so any attempt to get back to sleep or check the glowing contraption is thwarted. It takes some persistence, but I can see her resolve waning. I'm clearly too adorable to resist.

Next, I begin to meow pitifully, hoping she'll feel guilty for making me wait. I haven't eaten anything except the organic turkey kibble since dinner last night, and I'm practically wasting away over here. With big, sad eyes, I stare down at her intently. I make sure not to blink since that minimizes the impact. I can tell it's working, and she's beginning to move around a bit under the blanket. I consider taking the blanket in my teeth and making a run for my food bowl to see if she follows, but that seems like far too much effort. Now to seal the deal, I give one last meow and rub my face against hers. I do want food, but I also suddenly think about how much I love her. I have to make sure she smells like me so any other cats she encounters will know I have already staked my claim.

At my continued encouragement—some may call it nagging—she slowly rolls out of bed and plods noisily out to the food preparation area. I wind myself between her feet, rubbing lovingly against her bare legs, making sure they also smell like me, so those neighborhood stray cats know her legs are mine too. She opens the sacred cold box, which houses the food under lock and key. I let out an excited and impatient meow. Jackpot! I hear the top pop off a container and pace restlessly back and forth, eyes locked on her as she meticulously stirs some water into the food so it's soft but not runny. That is exactly how I like it, and Mom has been perfecting the precise formula for years. Locking on to my target, I leap up to the ledge where she's working, completely catching her off guard. I attempt to stick my face into the food for a long sniff. She's quick, though, snatching it away before I can sample it and telling me to get down. She always thinks I'm going to listen, but I decline and instead take a seat on the ledge. I glare at her as she holds the tantalizing food just out of range.

I try to exercise mind control by telling her, "Put the bowl down and walk away now!"

But alas, it doesn't work. I haven't perfected the technique yet, but I'm working on it and will not give up so easily.

She takes the bowl out into the hall, and I follow eagerly, meowing as I go. At last, she places the dish on the ground, and I approach with my mouth watering. I sniff once, twice, and realize, to my horror, that it's salmon. I sit back dejectedly and stare at the mushy fish food. I believe it's called pâté, which is the only variety of wet food I'll eat. Those chunky versions are disgusting. Do they actually expect me to bother chewing my food unnecessarily? Put it in a blender first, then bring it back and we'll reevaluate.

Mom is still watching me, so I turn my face upward with the saddest gaze that I can muster. She points to my food like I don't know it's there.

Telepathically, I tell her, "Yes, I know it's there, but waiter, I ordered tuna, and you appear to have made a grave mistake. Either that or there's salmon in my tuna today, and you know I hate when you blend flavors. I like my fish pure and unadulterated. It's sushi-grade only for me, and I'll accept nothing less. Take it away, and tell the chef to try again."

She points at the food once more, and I meow loudly, annoyed that we're even having this debate. The next stage of her training will focus on learning to obey commands the first time they are issued.

"Today, I feel like having tuna, and I won't be forced to eat this garbage," I respond. "Put it in the cold box for tomorrow when I might be in the mood for salmon, and I'll reconsider it then."

If only I had thumbs, I could do this myself, but alas, those containers are not cat friendly. I haven't quite worked out how to beat the complicated locking system, but one day I'll design a cunning machine to crack the code, and then I'll take a bite out of each container like my own gourmet tasting menu.

I can picture it now and hear myself saying, "Today I'll have the duck pâté appetizer, followed by roast chicken in gravy for my entree, and finish with the tuna in oil for dessert. Be sure to serve them in their own dishes so as not to mix flavors."

It has become a battle of wills, and I do my best to look adorable and sad. Mom crouches down to pet me. I make an approving noise, nosing her hand and trying to convey my displeasure while also reminding her that I should be spoiled to no end because I'm literally the cutest thing she's ever seen. After a few minutes of this standoff, she picks up the bowl and returns to the food preparation area. I hear her sorting through my stash of canned food. Success!

Magic Delivery Network

I had a busy afternoon lounging, alternating between the warm radiator and my cat tower with my fish toy snuggled against my chest. I love my tower and my toys. From the tower, I can survey my kingdom and pass along messages to my subjects below. Watching strangers in nearby apartments go about their boring lives is a nice pastime and helps me drift off into one of my four daily naps.

Occasionally, I see another cat or other beast staring back at me and think, "Who is this guy? Who let him into the building, and why was I not consulted?" I'll add it to my list of issues to discuss with management.

In the evenings, when I see the light begin to fade, I know Mom will be coming home soon. I take up a sentry position on the window ledge near the door and watch for her approach. Some days I wait patiently, others impatiently and taking a fifth nap can help pass the time. When I hear the ding and whooshing sound of the elevator, I get a sense of anticipation. Maybe it's Mom! Nope, just another delivery servant bringing food to someone down the hall. I really must figure out this service where, day or night, a minion brings the food of your choice to the door with no questions asked. How do I access this secret network? I'd have breakfast in the middle of the night, breakfast again at sunrise, breakfast again after a morning nap, lunch in the middle of the day, and so on. I start to daydream about dinner and temporarily forget that I'm watching for Mom. No, wait! I have to focus here. This is important work.

Lights begin to flicker on in other windows, and I occasionally spot movement, zeroing in intently from time to time to watch the evening rituals of the other humans milling about their homes. They never seem to utilize their window ledges as convenient perches, and I wonder why. Perhaps they are afraid of falling out. My tail hangs off the window sill, flicking slightly, as I enjoy the tranquility of a quiet evening at home. The circle on the wall makes a soft ticking noise that has a soothing, monotonous rhythm.

Then the ominous metal doors fly open again, and I hear footsteps approaching. My ears perk up, and my eyes go wide as I press my face against the window, focused and unblinking. At last, she has arrived!

She smiles and waves when she spots me in the window, and I let out a small meow even though I know she can't hear me. Excitedly, I hop down and race to the door just as it swings open. She bends down, strokes my back and coos softly. I rub enthusiastically against her hands and legs. I love her so much! I missed her, and I can't wait to snuggle while she watches the bright screen on the wall this evening.

I walk in circles around her and weave in between her legs as she moves inside, steps out of those things she

21

ties on her feet every morning, and drops her bags on the floor. Then she turns back, opens the door, and I get a sinking feeling that she's going to leave again. What! No! She's only just returned from wherever she goes all day long, and I need attention.

Then I realize there is a box sitting at the door. Another delivery minion must have come while I was sleeping today. I'm thoroughly intrigued. It's heavy, and she drags it inside with a grunt and begins to pry open the top. She removes some crinkly paper from inside and tosses it on the floor. I sniff it cautiously and watch with curiosity. Mom lifts out several heavy palettes, tears the plastic off, and there before me are dozens of cans of my favorite wet food. It's enough to feed an army! She has ordered from the enchanted delivery network on my behalf. I quickly take stock of the haul and turn to my toys scattered around the room.

"Here ye! Here ye! Today we have received a shipment of food that will provide us with nourishment for months to come. And by us, I mean me. I will need all hands on deck to catalog our spoils," I proclaim. "Look lively now!"

Mom holds a can out in front of me for a quality control inspection, and I aggressively rub my face against it, making sure it smells like me and is therefore mine. I meow and pace around the stacks of cans, while rubbing and sniffing them and trying to read the labels.

"This one is mine, and this one is mine, and this one is mine too!" I declare to no one in particular, but feel it must be said.

Oh, what a glorious day. Mountains of wet food all for me. I shall stack them in the shape of a throne and preside over them, joyfully selecting my food of choice each morning.

Once all the cans are accounted for, Mom carries them into the adjoining room, where she methodically organizes them by color and places them in a wooden box for safekeeping.

"Be careful; don't drop them," I think as I follow her to ensure it's done properly. This is now a risk management exercise. I always monitor the process, so no cans are lost or misplaced in transit. When everything is safely stowed away, we return to the empty box, and it appears that Mom is going to dispose of it.

"Wait!" I call, hoping she'll understand. "I hadn't noticed how wonderful this box was because I was distracted by the food, but I now realize that this is one of the most incredible boxes I've ever seen. I think it would make a great place to play and nap because it's square-shaped and deep enough for me to hide in, so no one could see me from the ground, only from overhead."

With great agility, I bound into the box and turn in a circle, sniffing and examining every angle until I have assessed its merits. Perfection! This will do. She has not only ordered me food but also a box that serves as a bed, playroom, and secret hideout. I peer over the top and survey the room. No other cat is in sight to challenge me for my conquest. Then I contentedly lie down, tucking my tail around me and checking the dimensions of the space for napping purposes.

Mom reaches in and pats my head. I have now claimed this as mine, and it will remain in the middle of the room until I deem it acceptable to move. It is only allowed to be relocated into the other room, where I can easily access it, but it will be out of the way, as Mom would probably say.

Suddenly, I hear a faint scratching sound coming from outside the box. What in the world could that be? I sit up and focus on the side where the sound is coming from. My tail twitches energetically. The scrapping continues, and then a blue, fuzzy face appears over the top of the box. It's Ms. Fish trying to climb in without my permission.

Like lightning, I reach out and smack her off the edge where she has perched. She goes sailing onto the floor below. Mom is crouching beside the box, watching the action. To my surprise, a moment later there's the sound again on the other side, and Ms. Fish pops her head up. She appears to be taunting me. I launch another attack, and she disappears below the edge. Her tail feather skitters along the top of the box, and I watch intently until her head reappears around the other side. She thought I wouldn't see her if she snuck up from behind, but she was wrong. I snag her with one paw and drag her into the box, proceeding to bite at the feather and kick her with my back claws.

Then I wait. She lies still in my paws, all fight having gone out of her. I watch her for a few moments, satisfied that I have asserted my dominance over the box, and it is once again all mine. As I ponder my superiority to the fish and mice in this house, I feel my eyelids drooping after a long fifteen minutes of supervising the food delivery and exploring and defending the box. I drift off into a peaceful sleep, the fish toy pressed tight against my chest.

Yoga

I love yoga. I love everything about it: the stretching, the lying on the floor, the squishy mat, the soothing music, all of it.

So, there I was this afternoon, taking my fourth nap on one of my many pillows, when Mom dutifully rolled out my hot pink yoga mat. I believe that exercise is part of a healthy lifestyle, so I wandered over to participate in the workout she had planned for today.

She begins by lying on her belly, bracing her hands against the floor, and lifting her body straight up before lowering herself back down again. When she lifts up, I rub my head against her chin and walk underneath her, flopping down at the top of the mat.

She looks at me like she's not sure what to do, but I give her a look back that says, "I'm not sure what you were expecting since we do this all the time, and by the way, what are you doing on my yoga mat?"

She scoots back so she can finish the exercise on the bottom half of the mat and not interfere with the spot that I have taken over. I stretch out and begin to focus on my breathing. Slow, steady breaths, filling my lungs to capacity and then exhaling all of the tension out of my shoulders, paws, and tail. With the next breath, I focus on relaxing my face and my ears because stress causes wrinkles and white fur. Mom is now jumping around and disrupting my rhythm. I try to ignore it, but the floor is shaking like a herd of elephants is in the room. I flex my paws and wiggle my tail, enjoying the sensation of the soft mat under me so much that I drift off into a brief power nap.

I am rudely awakened by Mom jumping again and breathing hard, but I feel refreshed and centered. I roll onto my stomach, tuck my feet underneath me, so it looks like I don't have any legs, and curl my tail around my body. I call this the cat pose. I watch with interest as Mom vigorously changes positions and makes soft grunting noises with each move. Sometimes she jumps, sometimes she sits up, and sometimes she just holds poses while shaking from the strain. This all looks silly to me, but I'm used to her bizarre habits by now, and they do provide a certain level of entertainment.

Her next move I call "fake sitting in midair." She pretends to sit, then stands back up, and repeats this process multiple times without ever actually sitting. I always worry that she's going to fall over and used to warn her that there wasn't anything underneath her to sit on. But she never falls, and I've come to accept this odd maneuver as part of her normal exercise regime.

I get to my feet, arch my back to stay loose, and wander over, rubbing against first one leg and then the other as she continues the motions. She manages to scratch my head during one of the reps, and I am so pleased. I walk in a circle around her and resume rubbing

27

against her shins. She moves to the other side of the mat and starts to hop. I also move back to that side, forcing her to stop so she doesn't land on me. As a reward for pausing, I resume rubbing and purring. She pats my head again, changes sides once more, and lies on her back with her knees up. She proceeds to sit up and lie back down, then sit up and lie back down. This move also confuses me, because if she wants to lie down, then she should just stay down, and if she wants to get up, she should just get up. I know she can get up since I've seen her do it on numerous occasions, but she seems content to make it halfway and then give up and lie back down.

The movement from one side of the mat to the other gives me a good workout as I follow her lead from side to side. I watch the new movement for a moment, time it just right, and step onto her chest as she lies down. I rub my face against her nose and cheek. She makes a soft sound, and I think my fur got in her mouth, but that's ok. Mom loves me so much, and I don't think that she minds. She strokes my cheeks a few times, and I purr loudly, letting her know that this is exactly what I wanted.

Mom eases me off to her side and onto the mat, scooting over and making space for me to lie next to her. She then keeps her back on the mat and proceeds to raise and lower her legs, almost touching them to the floor each time. I am content to count off the reps for her but then get bored at the count of three. I rise to my feet, and when her legs go up, I move directly underneath and lie down because that's my favorite side of the yoga mat.

She hovers her legs above me, unsure what to do now, then spins around so her legs face the opposite direction and the top of her head is beside me. She continues the up-and-down motion. I sniff her hair and make a contented little noise. I just love yoga.

Hidden Treasure

Mom thinks she can hide things from me. It's cute, and I let her believe she gets away with it. Currently, she is growing organic cat grass on top of the cold box where she stores food. Her goal is to keep it out of reach until it's tall enough for me to nibble the ends and rip pieces out by the roots. If it's in plain sight, I'll immediately eat the tender shoots as soon as they break through the dirt, and nothing will ever grow. This generally results in an empty pot of wet dirt. I'll admit that I lack some self-control when it comes to cat grass. I suppose we all have our faults.

I've been keeping an eye on the growth progress, stealthily watching her water it and turn it daily so all sides get equal sunlight. Today, I have decided that it is tall enough to withstand a little nibble. It can't hurt to sample it and make sure it's tasty. Mom has already left for the day, and I find that I'm hungry for a mid-morning snack. I wander out into the kitchen and crane my neck to stare up at the cold box. Despite my toned back legs and my uncanny ability to make impossible leaps, it's too tall for me to leap to the top. Instead, I hop easily onto the ledge where Mom prepares food, precariously walk along the edge of the sunken, metal tray that water drains into, and spring to the top of the cold box.

Life by Pumpkin: A Cat's View on Everything

There is a pot full of lush, green shoots that were lovingly grown just for me. I approach slowly and stick my nose into the center, breathing in the appealing scent of the fragile stalks. It's a beautiful sight. Then I begin to delicately nibble, being sure not to rip them out so they'll continue to grow back, and Mom will never know I've been up here. But they're so delicious that I can't help myself, and I begin to gorge on them, leaving bits of grass strewn everywhere.

When I'm satisfied, I jump down to the floor and take up a spot by the window, watching for movement in the other dwellings. Soon my stomach starts to grumble, and I feel a bit sick. Maybe I just need some water to wash down the greens. As I stroll over to my water bowl, I suddenly begin to heave, and up comes some partially digested foliage. I stare down at the liquidy, green pile on the floor. At that moment, the door opens, and Mom wanders in, pausing to assess the situation.

I stare up at her innocently as though to say, "What is this? Someone threw up on our floor while you were gone, and it absolutely wasn't me. You should probably prioritize cleaning this up."

I saunter into the small room off the hallway and hop into the large white trough where water rains down. I wait patiently as Mom takes those things off her feet and am tempted to rush over and swat the strings as she pulls them loose. She cleans up the regurgitated grass and follows me into the room to wash her hands. She notices me in the trough, and I give her an unblinking stare and lick my lips. She fills a small paper cup with water from the spigot, then leans over and slowly pours it out in front of me. I watch the water stream down the center of the trough and into a hole on one side. I look back up at her. She repeats this several times, and I just watch curiously. Finally, when I'm good and ready, I crouch down and, with the next pour, begin to daintily lap at the water as it flows by. I'm careful not to let it touch my paws, and if she ever pours it too fast so it splashes a little, I give her an angry look to express my displeasure with the poor service. She keeps up this process until I pause, stand up, and lick the water from the fur around my mouth. My stomach feels better now. Tomorrow I'll be ready for more grass, and we can do this again.

I rub against her leg to say thank you as I head to my cat tower to stare out the window for a while. I've been formulating a plan to conquer the other apartments in the building and take over their land and resources. I'm still in the information-gathering stage, which requires hours of careful observation each day.

Absorbing the Knowledge

I'm always looking to better myself and expand my horizons. Of course, I am already the smartest one in the kingdom, if not the world, but I still aspire to be a great scholar. That's why I spend so much time contemplating my extensive library of books, trying to absorb more knowledge.

Mom is lounging in my bed, reading a novel, and looking quite content. I watch her closely for a few minutes, tilting my head to one side and then to the other. Swiftly, I bounce across the springy surface and nudge her arm, encouraging her to scratch the top of my head. I pace back and forth across her lap while she nuzzles me and rubs my cheeks.

She puts the book down by her side, which means that it's my turn to use it. Casually, I stroll over and collapse on top of it, resting my head on the cover. I can feel the knowledge seeping in. I find that it helps if I close my eyes and take slow, even breaths while trying to meditate. I hear Mom sigh softly. She must be thinking about how committed and dedicated I am to my studies. Here I am, performing my due diligence on this Jane Austen lady and getting smarter by the minute. I could do this for hours.

Suddenly, I am startled awake by Mom gently easing herself out of bed in an attempt not to wake me. I'm a light sleeper, so no luck, but I appreciate the effort. I flick my ear to express my annoyance at being disturbed during my study time. Then I slightly open one eye to survey the landscape.

"What is this?" I wonder as a flash of red passes overhead. I perk up instantly. "What legendary fiend is this, and who allowed it into my domain? It must now be neutralized!" I will have to add the lack of security to my list of complaints for management.

I sit up and glance around. Again, the red streak goes whizzing by, and I realize it is circling above me. I roll to my back and try to snag it on the next pass, but it's too fast and manages to evade me. I flail my arms wildly, hoping to get lucky and catch it. I'm met with success, feeling it connect with the pad of one of my paws. I raise the other paw, hold on tight, and manage to clamp my teeth down on it. It's soft but unforgiving, and it continues to tug lightly, trying to free itself from my death grip. I chew it viciously but spit it out, as it doesn't taste like chicken or fish.

Then it slips away and wriggles across the blanket, heading for the edge of the bed. Getting to my feet, I crouch low, stalking it as it retreats for cover. It will not escape me today! I pounce, landing squarely on top of it, digging in my claws, and dragging it back across the bed. We roll back and forth as we struggle, and I soon find it wrapped around me. It's trying to strangle me, but I'm too smart for that.

I leap up and sprint off the bed, shedding the red fiend as I go. A moment later, I cautiously peek over the edge, surveying the situation. The attacker momentarily lies still before it begins to wriggle back and forth across the pillow. How dare it touch my pillow. It's mine! All mine! Only Mom has permission to handle my pillow.

Scampering back onto the bed, I launch an aerial attack, pinning the fiend to the pillow beneath my paws. I stomp on it madly, and it eventually stops tugging to get away.

I hear a knock at the door, but this is no time to get distracted. Mom silently picks up the book and slips from the room to see who has arrived. I wasn't done reading the book, but I'll express my displeasure over it later.

I warily eye my nemesis. It lies still, a red, tangled mess strewn across the bed and down onto the floor, where the rest of it is wound into a ball. Hmm, a ball!

I hop down and sniff the ball, circle around it, check for any other attackers, and give it a good swat. It rolls away from me, leaving behind a trail of red. I follow in hot pursuit. I whack it again, and it rolls under the bed, but there's no escaping me. There's not much clearance, but that's not a problem, as I can easily wiggle into small spaces. I squeeze underneath and continue to nudge the ball with my nose until I chase it out the other side. Then I take it in my jaws and race to the box that is still sitting in the hallway. In the privacy of my hideout, I diligently gnaw on my prize until I grow weary. I take my afternoon nap with my head resting atop it.

Secret Hideout Security Breach

I have a secret hideout in my closet. It's a small, square room with a cozy, fluffy pillow that I can nap on or lounge on while I contemplate the universe and all its mysteries. I'm the only one in the house who is small enough to squeeze through the door. It has a gate I can close to keep out the riff-raff or to let people know that I'm not to be disturbed. It's just a quiet place that's all mine, where I can go for some much-needed me time. There is even a convenient handle on top, so my minions can carry me around from place to place in complete comfort and style in a manner befitting my regal status.

So, one afternoon, I wandered into the room after patrolling the perimeter of my territory and checking for security breaches, only to find that my maid–I mean, my mom–had pulled the hideout from the closet, removed the fuzzy bed, and was scrubbing it down with sour-smelling cloths. She has the audacity to disturb my inner sanctum. Who gave her permission to touch my belongings?

"Stop this at once, and put everything back where you found it!" I demand, feeling incredibly put out.

I circle around her, sniffing and turning up my nose at the smell. I try to get closer, but she has wedged herself arm-deep through the door. I worry that she will get stuck, and then I'll never be able to use my hideout again. As she sits back on her heels, I move in and poke my head through the door, only to have her block my entrance. This is absurd.

I position myself a few feet back to keep an eye on the proceedings and make sure she doesn't do any lasting damage. She works quickly and smiles at me, but I only give her a hard stare in return. What if this had been my nap time? She didn't even ask me if I was about to take a nap in there.

She returns her attention to the pillow, running her hand back and forth and removing clumps of fur, before shaking it above a large white container where she disposes of the scraps. I don't break eye contact, ensuring that she doesn't try to throw it away with all of the fur that I worked so hard to coat it in. That's a solid three weeks of rubbing and rolling around to make sure it smells and looks a bit like me.

Satisfied, she squeezes the pillow back into the hideout and fluffs it a bit, which I do appreciate. Seizing the opportunity, I lunge forward, slipping past her through the door, and hunker down inside, staring out with an expression that says, "What?"

She pats my head and slides the room back into the closet, adjusting the position so the gate can open fully without hitting anything or getting in the way. I enjoy the ride, and I look out the holes in the walls. What an efficient mode of transportation!

Life by Pumpkin: A Cat's View on Everything

In here, I feel like a spy, elusive and out of sight unless I want to be seen. I can see everyone else, but unless they know where to look, they don't see me. From my position and with some patience, I will learn everyone's dirty secrets and use those against them at opportune times, especially when I want a can of food and it's not dinner time yet. Oh, the things I will accomplish from this vantage point.

Leslie Popp

Games We Play

I like things to be tidy. That's why I'm diligent about brushing my hair and thoroughly washing my face every afternoon. The top of my head is always the toughest spot, but I never forget behind my ears. I have devised a clever system to reach the tricky spots. I daintily lick one paw, then tuck my chin down, stretch my paw as far up on my head as I can reach, and rub back and forth, folding my ear forward and straightening my fur. Then I lick my paw again and repeat. I keep my eyes closed so I don't accidentally get a claw in them, and when I'm done with one side, I switch to the other. Mom sometimes stares while I'm doing this and goes, "Aww."

I am just finishing my daily routine when Mom strolls by with the tall basket she fills with her human fur. It is a covering she puts on and takes off every day that comes in many different colors and textures. This fur is placed into a basket when dirty, then taken somewhere secretly, and comes back warm and clean. She's such a diligent little worker, always making sure my home is in order. I follow her to oversee the operation, and when she takes the top off the basket, I am delighted to see that my sheets are clean. I wonder if they're still warm. When she turns her back, I launch myself up and into the basket, landing softly in the pile of sheets. Yes! They're

40

still warm, and that's just delightful. I breathe in deeply and nestle in, getting a fresh coat of fur all over them.

Mom kisses the top of my head and wanders away. This is our routine. She brings me an offering of clean sheets in a basket, which is just as good as an empty box, if not better, and I relax in them, letting the warmth loosen up my tight muscles. Jumping on and off various platforms, ledges, and beds is quite a workout. Some days, it's nice to just kick back and relax.

I flick the end of my tail contentedly and listen to her moving from one room to the next, cleaning and straightening as she goes. I shall have to give her a soft meow and a nose touch as a thank you.

When I've had my fill of the basket, I hop out, which is more difficult than getting in because the sheets are so soft, and I don't have a solid surface to use as a launch pad. But I'm an athlete, trained in the high and long jumps, so I manage. Mom notices me padding across the wood floor to assess her work and quickly scurries away to put the sheets back on the bed before I decide to nap in them again.

I quickly follow because there is a game I love called *I Want To Lie In Bed, And You Want To Put The Sheets On*. She is familiar with the rules, and with lightning speed, she has managed to put the stretchy sheet on already. Well, my wits are just as quick, and I leap onto the bed and collapse in the center. She pauses a moment, paces from one side to the other, then tosses the second sheet into the air and lets it parachute down on me gently.

41

I wait a moment, letting the anticipation build, and pretend that I'm not bothered at all. She straightens the sheet, and as it glides over me, my fur stands on end. So much for brushing it just now and getting my ear hair to stand up at the tip in the latest fashion.

I army crawl around under the sheet, burrowing through the fabric and following her movements as I hear her going one way and then the other. She can run, but she can't hide. I'm invisible now, and she'll never see me coming.

Next, I feel the blanket settle over me, and I have to work a bit harder as I crawl around, forging new tunnels that quickly collapse behind me as I go. Now I'm sure my fur is really sticking up, but that's a problem for later.

I hear a scratching sound at the bottom of the bed and wiggle toward it, reaching out and clutching at the sheets where I see movement. I manage to grab whatever it is through the fabric and hold on tight, but it pulls away, and I take off in pursuit as I hear it scrambling toward safety. Then something touches me, and I roll onto my back, my paws bunching up the linen, and try to get my arms around whatever it is. It periodically makes an unfamiliar sound and occasionally touches the spot where I've lifted a paw and tented the sheets. I try to swat at it, but it always skitters away.

I'm starting to get hot and decide that I'm the winner of this game today. I wriggle to the side of the bed and slide to the floor, afraid to look at my fur in the reflective surface by the closet. I set to work licking my paw and rubbing my head, satisfied that my bed is in order, in large part due to my efforts.

I notice Mom has moved on to folding the human fur that had been buried in the depths of the basket. The bottom drawer of the large storage box, where she keeps all of her fuzzy human furs, is open. I have learned that this particular type of covering is reserved for cold weather. It comes in so many different colors, and I assume it must be some clever signaling system used to convey messages to the other humans. I scoot between her feet and nonchalantly hop into the drawer. There are a few too many of these furs in here for it to be a comfortable fit, but no matter, I can throw some on the ground. I begin to paw at them, creating a space to lie down by scattering them in every direction.

Mom tries to stop me, but I suddenly hunker down and give her the cutest, most innocent face that I can muster, with my eyes wide and my ears perked up. All she does is pat my head, and instead of filling my drawers, she starts hanging things in the closet. When I'm done with my drawer, she can put the furs back in and refold the ones I displaced to create the ideal lounge spot. I know she likes all the orange fur I get on the dark-colored ones. I think it gives them some character.

Working Hard

I work so hard. Sometimes I spend hours squinting in front of the hinged device with the bright screen that fits conveniently on Mom's lap. I think clever thoughts that no one has thought of before because I'm obviously smarter than everyone else. I prefer to work in bed in the evenings because that's where I do my best thinking. I can be extremely focused, and I'm content with my work. I suspect I'm a model leader and the best at my job. No one has ever had anything negative to say about me.

Tonight, for example, I am working from Mom's lap, with the top half of me draped across her leg and the bottom half stretched out on the blanket. This position is good for my back and helps maintain my flexibility. If I start to feel stiff, I stretch my front paws out in front of me as far as they can go, placing them firmly on the lighted screen while I arch my back.

Mom is carefully balancing the folding contraption on her other leg, so it's in the optimal viewing position for me. She is hunched over me at an awkward angle, furiously tapping the small black squares connected to the device. I mainly dictate my musings and instructions to her since my paws are small, and I don't have thumbs, so it's hard for me to use the contraption on my own.

Occasionally, when I spot a mistake, I reach out and place one paw on the black squares as if to say, "No, no, no. Go back and check it again."

I flick my tail contentedly because tonight we're really chugging along. The white screen is quickly filling up with black scribbles, and I'm finally feeling like I've hit my stride. A few more hours, and my memoirs will be ready for the publisher.

I'll be so far ahead of schedule that they'll all bow down to me and say, "Oh, please, master Pumpkin, can you please be the top cat at the company and show us how you are so super productive and amazing at this job?"

If I'm feeling generous, I'll explain my ways, but not at first. They have to earn the privilege. You can't just go around handing out sage advice to anyone, or they'll think they're special and keep asking you for things. No, first they have to do something for me, and we'll go from there.

Time for a stretch! As I reach out my paws and breathe in a deep, calming breath, the light screen slowly shifts just out of my reach. I stretch further, but again it slides away. What is this crafty nonsense? Annoyed, I roll to my feet and step over Mom before turning in a circle and taking up a very similar position on her other leg. She shifts the contraption to make room and resumes tapping as I mentally dictate the next chapter to her.

I blink slowly and think of all the people and cats that will read about me one day. I'll be so famous, and they'll all sit around admiring me and wishing they were me. There can only be one of me, though! I imagine them all cheering my name and running to the windows to catch a glimpse of me as I am carried through the streets in celebration.

I begin to purr softly and then think, "Make sure to include a page about how I am the world's most musically inclined cat, whose purr is always in tune."

Culinary Lessons

I'm a very particular eater. Some might call me discerning. I can't help that I have such a refined palate and a heightened sense of smell. I have trained Mom to stock only cans of fish and chicken, with an occasional duck mixed in when I'm feeling exotic.

My food must be blended into a smooth consistency. I can't stress that enough. If it's only finely chopped, then I just look at it in disgust until Mom opens another can or smashes it into a paste for me. I don't feel like this is a difficult task, yet on rare occasions, she gets it wrong. Anyway, dinner tonight was exactly how I like it. Chicken with a hint of gravy was served in a small white bowl placed precisely on top of a soft, clean cloth to catch any spills.

Mom's diet is very different from mine. I've never understood her eating habits. She appears to prefer gross foods that are leafy and green or other unusual colors rather than chicken, duck, or fish. Despite my disappointment in her tastes, I'm always curious about her food and want to make sure she eats a healthy diet so she lives a long life and continues to do my bidding for many days to come.

She just sat down to dinner at the large wooden table, and I pad silently across the room, catching her by surprise when I leap up beside her. Mom leans her head down, and we nuzzle our foreheads together before touching our noses. There is so much love in this house.

I draw in a deep breath, dissecting the aroma of her food and picking apart the various scents. Curiously, I inch forward, my whiskers twitching as I sniff the selection. This is all part of our routine. She makes food, I investigate the meal to see if I want it and to make sure it's safe to consume, and then we dine together. I circle the plate, getting steadily closer until I'm hovering right above the steaming dish. My whiskers almost touch it, but they don't.

I pause there to process all of the new information my nose is taking in before closing my eyes and shaking my head in disgust. I shudder and am baffled that she voluntarily eats this stuff. She can open cans of cat food at any time and have as much as she wants. Instead, she eats this garbage with no hint of chicken, duck, or fish. Those are really the only three food groups that matter, and she seems to ignore them entirely. I don't know how she keeps herself going on this diet.

Done with my assessment, I stretch out and settle in to keep her company during dinner. She pulls out the chair beside her in case I want my own seat, but I'm comfortable here for now. I appreciate the gesture, but I prefer to lie right in front of her, where I get maximum attention. The chair is also lower than the table, and I like to be up high, where I can survey my domain and hand out orders more easily.

Life by Pumpkin: A Cat's View on Everything

Suddenly my mood changes, and I roll over, stretch, and hop down onto the empty chair. Carefully, I slip underneath Mom's arm and onto her lap. Instinctively, she lowers that arm to hold me so I don't fall off. I turn in a small circle and ease down on my side, with my head resting on her arm. Dutifully, she cradles me to her chest, and I close my eyes contentedly. She is so nice and warm, and I'm at peace when we're close together like this.

Mom continues on with dinner, using only one hand to eat now, but this is why she has two.

Winged Fiend

I am lounging on the ledge by the window with my tail wrapped around me, the tip flicking gently as I survey my domain. All is quiet. Not another human or cat is stirring in the apartment windows across the way. The day is sunny, and I love basking in the warmth. It's just another lazy afternoon. As I am beginning to wonder what's for dinner, I see movement out of the corner of my eye. For a brief moment, I almost thought it was an illusion or a figment of my imagination.

Instantly, my ears perk up, straining to hear any sound of an intruder. My eyes grow wide, and I press my cheek against the invisible barrier that keeps me contained in the apartment, trying to get a better view. Everything is still. I remain silent, not daring to move a muscle, completely focused, and patiently awaiting whoever is lurking nearby.

Suddenly, a fiend with grayish feathers and beady eyes hops into view on the ledge. It is on the other side of the barrier and hasn't spotted me yet. It bobs its head, turns in a circle, and fluffs its feathers out. I crouch down, almost involuntarily, and my eyes lock on the target, calculating the distance and deciding if I can reach it in one pounce. It's outside of my range, but it's heading this way, and based on the trajectory and the wind speed, it will pass within striking distance of my current position. I mentally send the signal for my mouse and fish armies to mobilize.

"Mouse forces to the right! Fish to the left! Wait for my signal to attack!" I proclaim, having complete faith that they will obey.

The stranger continues to wander about aimlessly, totally unaware of the danger. Something deep within me awakens. It feels primal and cold, and suddenly I realize that I am a mighty hunter. I am a jungle cat, stalking his prey in the wilderness, where there are no cans of food for my dinner. I must bring down this tasty morsel with my own two paws or risk waiting until breakfast to eat. I have never seen a chicken up close before, but I hope this is my chance.

The intruder makes an odd cooing noise, and I am captivated. My mouth opens slightly, and I respond with a soft, cackling sound, my chin fluttering. I worry that it heard me, but it continues the slow strut without a care in the world. Occasionally, it pecks at the ledge and tilts its head oddly to one side and then the other.

It delicately shuffles along the narrow walkway, looking up and across at the other windows, paying no attention to me. It's getting closer and closer until it's just inches away, and my mouth is starting to water.

Then we are side by side. It is directly across the barrier, and I remain perfectly still, barely breathing, and waiting for the perfect moment. When it looks up, I swiftly lift a paw and swat at it fiercely, hoping to knock it senseless and pounce to hold it down until it submits to my will. I know this is the right thing to do because something inside of me remembers my ancestors' ancient art of hunting.

Alas, despite my impeccable timing and the strength of my paw, I connect only with the invisible barrier, creating a thumping sound that startles my prey and causes it to frantically fly away. I watch as it disappears from view, feeling confused and frustrated. I was so sure I had it. How could it have escaped?

Drat! I must break free of these invisible barriers! They are preventing me from reaching my full potential as King of the World. One day, when I bust out of this place, I shall conquer the civilization of those feathery fiends just beyond my current reach. If they fail to submit to me, I will not be merciful. I will eat well for days and wear a crown of beaks. Then they will have no choice but to bow down to me and fly into my bowl at dinner time. I aspire to do what no tabby cat before me has ever dared to do!

Also, mental note, tomorrow I will learn how to fly. That seems like a much more efficient way to travel. On that note, I turn to my climbing tower, where Mousey is still perched from our earlier snuggle. He is looking at me with those dark, unblinking eyes, not responding at all to my telepathic commands to get out of my sight since he and his troops failed to execute their orders. He just lies there looking at me, not even bothering to apologize for his incompetence. Frustrated, I reach out and smack him harshly, sending him flying across the room.

I feel a bit better after that discipline, and I hop onto my tower to cool off. Ms. Fish is lying on the ground beneath me, and I give her a withering stare. I hope she learned a lesson from what I just taught Mousey. Let this be a warning to never disappoint me again.

Test Number 12

Mom and I have designated snuggle time every night. In my opinion, it's from the time she comes home to the time she leaves in the morning. The problem is that it's hard to convince her to stay in one place for very long. She's always getting up to do things around the apartment, and she's proving not to be very trainable in this regard. We've been working on "Sit!" and "Stay!" commands for a while, but it hasn't been terribly effective. I'm considering other approaches, but let's just call it a work in progress. I am an extremely intelligent cat, so I have complete confidence that I'll be able to accomplish it eventually. It's just a question of how and when. Luckily, I have plenty of time on my paws to consider new methods while she's away all day.

This journal entry is documenting test number 12. It's dark outside, and the test subject is resting in bed watching the blinky screen on the wall that makes a lot of noise. I am curled up by her side with my head propped up on her shoulder, watching carefully for signs of movement or intent to move. It's cozy and warm here, and I don't want to be disturbed.

Before going to sleep, she always gets up, goes into the small room nearby with the running water, and cleans her teeth with some kind of smelly paste that results in stinky breath. Yuck! She needs to have some tuna juice afterward.

Suddenly, she begins to sit up, and the moment of truth has arrived. Swiftly, I crawl up onto her chest and stare at her with wide eyes, employing the tried and tested approach that conveys, "Oh, I'm so adorable; do everything I say, and don't inconvenience me ever!"

She pauses and lies back down, gently petting me and murmuring softly. It's very calming, and I start to purr. But I can't lose focus. The subject seems to have been subdued for the moment. Count this as a win.

A few blissful minutes pass, and I am lulled into a stupor by the consistent petting. But then I feel her begin to shift again, and my eyes fly open. The subject is attempting to slide out from underneath me. What a crafty move. It's time to employ a new tactic.

I reach out with both paws and press them against her cheeks while thinking, "Stay down! We're having a beautiful moment here; don't ruin it!" I want her to be still and just enjoy my presence.

This makes her pause again, and she is quiet for a moment before reaching up and moving my paws down to her shoulders. But I am persistent and move them back to her chin, trying to literally hold her down. She places them back on her shoulders, so I put them on her neck, experimenting to see what is most effective. We continue to play this game, and I try digging in my claws a little bit and placing one paw on her face and the other on the hand that keeps moving. It becomes a battle of wills, and I think I might be winning.

I try the two-paws-on-the-cheek approach again, and to my delight, she doesn't move them. Mom sighs softly, places both hands on my back, and pats me lovingly. I wait, not wanting to declare success too soon. After a few minutes, I slowly remove my paws and tuck them underneath me in my preferred nap position. I watch her face for any signs of deception, but her eyes are now closed, and she's breathing evenly.

The test seems to have been successful. The subject has fallen asleep during the procedure. I'll repeat the strategy tomorrow to see if the same result is achieved.

I rest my head on her chest and doze off, listening to her heartbeat.

A Welcome Tribute

It's nice to have friends who adore you and just want to make you happy. I had a bunch of them over last night, and we were up super late, partying until the middle of the night, when we cheered loudly and hugged each other. Everyone was dressed so nicely to impress me, and they "oohed" and "ahhed" over me constantly. This is what it's like to be a celebrity. They all want to be my friends. But they sometimes forget that the way to a cat's heart is through his stomach, and not one of them brought me a fish as an offering.

I had to alter my schedule for the party since the middle of the night is when I'm most likely to be on the prowl. Usually, it's quiet, and I can stalk Fish or Mousey on stealthy feet to my heart's content. But last night it was far too noisy, and there wasn't time in my busy social schedule to allow for prowling around and spying on the neighbors. I'll just have to double my efforts tonight.

As usual, I awoke this morning bright and early. No late-night shenanigans can disrupt my wake-up time. In the faint morning light, I stroll about, casually assessing the mess that my mom will need to clean up for me this morning. It looks manageable, and no one disturbed my food or water or used my litter box, so any crisis has been averted.

In the next room, I encounter something truly disturbing. I notice movement as I turn the corner and dash under one of the chairs. I hold perfectly still, so whatever it is doesn't see me. I'm scared since I didn't hear it come in last night. How could this happen? How could something get past my impenetrable defenses? I don't know exactly what it is, but it must have entered on silent feet. It could be an alien, a monster, or some kind of robot that has gained sentience and is rebelling against us. Whatever it is, it has to go!

I consider jumping on Mom, but then I worry about her safety and don't want to wake her. No, I can't turn my back on this thing, or it might attack! I'll just have to take it down on my own. Now is the time to defend my territory.

I rush out and leap at the invader. I land a swift smack, but it flies away and bounces off the wall before coming back toward me, seemingly unmoved and unafraid. I retreat under the table used for human meal times and watch as it drifts around the room, hovering a few feet from the ground and dragging a string behind it. It moves aimlessly about before slowing down and remaining suspended above the couch. I watch the string as it grazes the floor, and I wonder what kind of trap this is. The thing doesn't appear to have eyes, so I can't tell if it's looking at me or not.

Life by Pumpkin: A Cat's View on Everything

Silently, I creep toward the invader, pressed low to the ground with my eyes wide and ears angled forward. The thing continues to sway slightly, and I find it unnerving. I watch cautiously, but it doesn't appear to be preparing for an attack. I can't make out any arms or legs, and I wonder who tied the string to it. It's round, a bit shiny, and an unnatural color.

Gaining confidence, I inch forward until I am next to the couch. Still, it remains suspended there, not seeming to care that it's being stalked. I stretch out my neck and sniff at the string. It smells like something I've encountered before, maybe something artificial. I hop up onto the couch, and now it's only slightly above my head. It wobbles a little with my approach. I freeze, waiting for it to make another move. It drifts lazily away and stops after a few inches. I approach warily, but the sense of danger is easing.

It's now directly above my head, and I sniff at it curiously. It has an odd smell but doesn't resemble any living thing I have ever encountered. I don't hear a heartbeat or see it breathing, and I realize this thing might not be alive at all. Perhaps it's a toy–something someone gave me last night for the purpose of dragging my string around and amusing me when Mom isn't available to do the job. To confirm, I reach up, gently swat it, and sure enough, it drifts away with the string following obediently.

What excellent friends I have!

Banishment

I have been banished from my own room! This is not allowed in my house, as all rooms are mine and no doors should ever be shut. Everyone should be well trained and do as I say.

"Open this door at once!" I demand in frustration.

Let me explain how this happened. The night started off just like any other night. Mom turned off the lights and settled into bed. I walked across her belly and tucked myself up against her left side, which is my preferred side. I can't explain it, but I must be left-pawed or something.

Anyway, I began my nightly ritual of gently kneading her upper arm. I positioned myself with my back against her side and my head on her shoulder, leaving all of my paws free to move. Then I began to gently press my front paws into her arm, creating a soothing rhythm. As I relaxed and settled into full snuggle mode, my back paws involuntarily adopted the cadence of my front paws. It's very relaxing to concentrate on the tempo of the right paw, left paw, back paws, right paw, left paw, and back paws. Mom was so warm, and after a few minutes, I began to drift off into a deep sleep.

If the kneading doesn't put me to sleep, she kisses the top of my head and gently pats me on the back, as if to say, "That's enough kneading; just go to sleep little one."

I don't know how she does it, but it usually does the trick. I get very cranky and can be persistent if I don't get at least five minutes of kneading time. I meow loudly and angrily if anyone disrupts me.

Tonight went smoothly, and we were resting quietly in each other's arms when suddenly I awakened, and all of my senses were on alert. I looked around, but nothing seemed amiss. I walked the perimeter of the room, but everything appeared to be in order. I was wide awake and decided to jog a few laps around the room to put my jumping ability to the test and burn off some of the excess energy.

I sprang from the floor to the bedside storage box and trotted across the headboard at the top of the bed. I'm such a stealthy little thing! I slid off the other side and down to the floor. Then I hopped back onto the bottom of the bed and leapt up to the tall storage box with many drawers that sits against the far wall. I was afraid of slipping on a piece of paper lying atop the box during my next go-round, so I pushed it onto the floor, making a bit of a racket. As it turns out, it was a stack of papers. Mom stirred, but I quickly continued on my way, not wanting her to think I was responsible for the noise. I launched from the tall storage box back to the bed, then to the floor, and then I began the circuit again. This time I raced across the tops of the pillows.

Mom whispered something, but I couldn't pause to chat. I was a cat on a mission, racing from the floor to the bedside box to the pillows and back to the floor as the cycle continued. On the third or fourth turn, Mom reached out and wrapped her arms around me to stop my trajectory. I took a moment to sniff and nuzzle her brow because I adore her. She released her hold, thinking I was settling in again, but I was too restless for that. I leapt up and began my circuit training again, trying to beat my best time.

She said something in a harsher tone, but I couldn't be bothered or interrupted right now. Couldn't she see that I was training for the cat Olympics? I will be faster, stronger, and cuter than all the other cats. I will be crowned and presented with a bowl of finely ground tuna on command.

I was lost in my thoughts and didn't notice Mom sitting up. On my next pass over the top of the bed, she caught me, hoisted me into her arms, and hopped up with surprising speed and agility. I was stunned for a moment, but I also loved being so high in the air. From her shoulder, I could rule over everything beneath me. She really should get a perch to wear on her head and carry me around in style wherever she goes.

To my surprise, she opened the bedroom door, set me just outside, and closed it quickly so I couldn't dart back in between her feet. I was momentarily confused and left standing all alone.

Now I'm stuck out here and contemplating my next move. How did this happen? How dare she! I assess the situation for a minute and think, "Well, if I can't sleep, neither will she."

I am so sad about being separated from her by this door. If only I were taller and my paws could turn that handle thing, we wouldn't have this issue. I'll have to talk to Mousey about having a lower handle installed.

I let out my loudest, most pitiful meow and wait for a response. Nothing. I do it again and again, and then I begin to make up a song. From inside the room, I hear, "SSSSSHHHHH," but I don't know what that means. I know she's listening to me, though, and I'm sure soon she's going to realize that I'm locked out. I bet she's missing me already.

So, I keep up the song, and I paw at the door a bit to see if it will budge. It's pretty solid, but the pawing makes a pleasing noise, so I add some percussion to my tune. I place my front paws on the door, balancing on my back legs, and rapidly smack them against the wood, taking satisfaction in the thumping sound they make. I'm feeling like a musical genius right about now with the background beat of the door and the melody of the meowing. Occasionally, I pause to listen and see if Mom can hear me. I definitely detect some stirring.

I go back to the door, tapping and singing, and after a few minutes, just as I am reaching the refrain again, I hear footsteps. My ears perk up, and I lower my front paws to the ground. The door cracks open, and I rush through the tiny crack. I am so happy to see Mom again. It has been a long fifteen minutes, and I thought I would never get back in. Enthusiastically, I rub against her shins, winding back and forth between her feet and pausing to sniff her knee.

She picks me up again and holds me tight, pressing her cheek against mine. I hold still, loving every moment of being close to her. Then she places me back on the bed and crawls in beside me. I begin the kneading process again before drifting off until morning, when she will need to be awakened for breakfast.

Supervising My Kingdom

Sometimes I take Mom for a walk and let her explore the rest of my kingdom. It's a lazy morning, and I decided that it would be good for both of us to stretch our legs a bit. She opens the front door, and we stroll cautiously out into the hallway, making sure that no one else is about. The coast is clear.

I eagerly sniff along the walls and the floor, investigating every inch. A good ruler knows his domain from top to bottom. I pick up the scent of several other subjects that live behind the other doors and of the tiny, yappy beast that I dislike but tolerate as long as I don't see him. There are so many things to look at out here and so many different smells.

I do think we should redecorate this area. It could use a few soft pillows and tall perches, and there's not a food or water bowl in sight. I don't like being this far from my bowls in case I get the urge to snack.

I hop up into the window and perch on the narrow ledge, showing off my strong legs and expert balancing ability. I can see back into our home from this vantage point, and it looks so cozy in there. No one is stirring in any of the other windows, but humans are lazy, and some days they sleep so late. I don't understand why they are awake all day and asleep all night. I think they have it backward.

Finding nothing of interest to keep my attention, I return to prowling along the floor. There are many doors in this area, and I have to approach and assess each one in turn. I check for new smells and listen for movement or talking within to see if my subjects are in attendance for my patrol.

I am careful not to disturb or scare my subjects, so I don't meow and demand entrance to each of their homes. I am a considerate ruler and only require periodic check-ins when they least suspect it. I don't want them to know that I'm out here because that's the best way to evaluate them in their natural habitat. What if one was planning a rebellion? They certainly wouldn't risk talking about it while I was nearby. But if I show up unannounced on silent feet and listen in at their door, I might just catch them in the treasonous discussion.

I am in no hurry, and I have all the time in the world to snoop. Periodically, I look back over my shoulder to make sure the door to my own residence is still open, and finding that it is, I continue on my way. I wander from door to door and catch the scent of some meat cooking. Someone must be preparing an offering for me. I probably won't eat it, though, because only Mom knows how I like my food served and seasoned.

As I double back toward home, I come to the door with the noisy beast. We pause here, and I listen intently. I hear light footsteps within, and they are heading right

66

for our location. I freeze, not sure if the yappy thing has heard me. Mom doesn't seem to understand why we're silently standing here and asks me something. She completely blows my cover, and the yappy devil raises an ear-splitting alarm. I hiss in return, and the hair on my back stands up. I could totally take that little pipsqueak, but today I'm feeling merciful, and there is a door between us. I hiss again for good measure, and I hear people moving about now.

We will fight another day, and I make a hasty retreat down the hall. Mom follows as I lead her back to the comfort and safety of our home. I do not relax until she closes the door and locks it behind us.

Overall, I would call that a success. Everything seems to be humming along smoothly, and I caught no one plotting to challenge my authority. Mom dutifully stayed by my side, following a few steps behind wherever I led her. I would say her training is going well, and she is showing great promise. All we need to do now is work on her stealth.

Leslie Popp

Water Is My Nemesis

Water is my nemesis. From as early as I can remember, we've just never gotten along. It's wet, it messes up my fur, and I can't stand the sight of it. Water should only exist within the confines of my designated bowl and in the cups that Mom diligently pours into the big white trough, so it flows right in front of me, never touching my paws. This allows me to drink at my leisure or watch it go down the hole in the floor if I so choose.

Mom doesn't seem to share my feelings, and every day she actually plays in the water. Ewwww! I don't know why she does it or how she can tolerate the feeling. If water just fell from the sky on me, I would run and hide under the bed, in my secret hideout spot in the closet, under the human's mealtime table, or anywhere that was protected from the water.

I like to stay close by, but not too close, when she's in the water to ensure she's okay. I don't know what I would do if there was an emergency and I had to get her out. So far, all has gone smoothly, and I've gotten used to this weird habit, but honestly, I can't support it. If she wanted to be clean every morning, she should just do what I do and take up a systematic cleaning routine that starts with licking her paws and then wiping down the

68

top of her head. This removes dirt and styles your fur at the same time, and there is absolutely no water involved. I've tried suggesting this, but she doesn't seem to understand. Sometimes, I even demonstrate first thing in the morning, but she hasn't learned this skill yet. I'll keep trying.

Anyway, I've finished my breakfast and am content for the moment. Mom just disappeared into the room with the ceiling water and closed the door, but I meow loudly, and she opens it again so I can slip in. I know the routine by now, and I settle onto the comfy floor mat to wait it out.

Water begins to fall, and I try to focus on other things. Tuna. Soft blankets. Mousey. Feathers. Chicken. Cat grass. Mom reaches her hand in and tests out the water to see if it's to her liking. I'm never sure what she's looking for because no water is to my liking. Finding it satisfactory, she steps in and closes a sheet, so I can't see her anymore. I cringe at the thought of my fur being wet.

I'm curious if she closes the sheet because she's embarrassed that I'm seeing her without her fur. I don't understand how she can take her fur off or why it's always different colors from day to day. It's very weird fur and not nearly as soft and beautiful as mine, but then no one's fur is as soft as mine.

I hear a noise, like she has pushed some heavy object off a ledge, and I worry that something has gone terribly wrong. I rise slowly to my feet, debating whether I am willing to get closer to the falling water to investigate the situation. I tell myself to be brave and inch forward. When I reach the sheet, I place my front paws up on the slippery edge and peek my head around to peer in. Mom sees the movement and coos at me. I really like that she's happy to see me, but then a tiny drop of water lands on my paw, and I make a hasty retreat, shaking that paw in disgust.

I limp back to my mat and diligently clean that paw, making sure I have removed all the pesky water and my fur is smooth again. Once satisfied, I settle in and wait.

A few minutes pass, and the water stops. I heave a sigh of relief and watch expectantly as Mom continues with the morning ritual, which involves bottles of smelly stuff that she puts on her face and eyes. I don't know what the purpose of all this is, but I oblige her silly habits and am always patient.

At last, she pulls on a new type of fur and is ready to face the day. I wander off to find Ms. Fish. She's a really good listener when I just need to vent about my water-related stresses.

Establishing Dominance

Mom has a male friend. He's been around a lot recently and seems to really like me, but the question is: do I like him? You don't wander into my house and automatically get to be friends with me. We're only friends if I say we're friends.

He gets down on the ground to pet me, play with me, and sometimes even feed me. He's open to snuggles, which does, admittedly, win him some points. But I'm still evaluating him. I'm not convinced that this isn't some crafty ploy to undermine my authority in the house and muscle in on my time with Mom. I am the favorite. I am the man of this house, and there's only room for one of us unless I say so!

So here he is again today, stretched out on my side of the bed and using one of my pillows. He seems to think he's going to be allowed to stay here tonight, but I haven't approved of this arrangement. If he must remain in this house, then he can sleep on the floor at the end of the bed like a good boy until I decide he has earned a place on my bed, which may never happen.

They're talking quietly, and Mom seems really happy. Her smile always warms my heart, but I remember not to let my guard down. I don't want us to get attached to this guy in case he turns out not to be house-trained or social and we have to send him back.

I hop onto the bed and stroll between them. Mom pats the top of my head, making me feel special and fuzzy inside. I slowly turn toward her, which results in my backside being right in his face. I make sure my tail is lifted all the way up.

"Take a good look, buddy!" I think to myself, feeling quite pleased. I press my forehead against Mom's, prolonging this beautiful moment, then walk right onto her chest and curl up into a tight ball.

I make sure I am facing her new friend so I can stare him down periodically and make sure he knows his place. I have to keep an eye on this one.

He says something to me and reaches out, gently scratching the spots I have trouble reaching on the back of my head and neck. It's disarming, and I drop my guard for a moment, letting out an involuntary purr. Then I catch myself and focus on not purring and looking annoyed, even though that spot was a little itchy.

Once they're asleep and unaware, I creep up close to his head and sniff him. He smells different than Mom, but I'm not sure if his distinct odor is normal or if I should be worried about this. I study his face, which now looks so innocent despite his attempts today to encroach on my territory. He seems vulnerable in this deep sleep, and I make a mental note of that for use against him at a later date. I walk right across him, and he doesn't stir at all. That's a good sign.

I want to sit on the bedside storage box, but I realize he has put several of his things on it. They're scattered haphazardly, and there is no place for me to sit. I pause to consider the situation for a few minutes and tell myself not to make any rash moves. But how inconsiderate of him to just lay claim to my space!

I reach out and gently nudge one of the items toward the edge. It slides softly, and a rebellious spark ignites within me. I glance back at him and then push it off. It clatters to the floor, and Mom rolls over, but he doesn't move. Mom is clearly the superior human, with enhanced senses. I step forward and reach out to knock off the glowing, rectangular thing that everyone is always staring at. I use one paw and then switch to the other, slowly nudging it here and there until it just happens to fly off. This makes a much louder sound, and they are both startled awake.

Quickly, I hop to the ground and walk away from the scene of the crime, trying to look bewildered and like I too was just rudely awakened by the noise. Mom calls my name.

I act like, "Oh, hey, I heard that sound too, and I have no idea where it came from, but don't worry; I'm going to look into it right now, so just go back to sleep."

I hear the man retrieve his things and put them back up on the storage box, like he thinks I'm not going to double back once he's asleep and knock them right back down on the floor where they belong. And so, the mind games begin.

Unapproved Beasts

I'm sitting in the window, gazing out at my kingdom, and wondering what to do with the rest of my afternoon. The options include stretching out on the heater to bask in the warmth or snuggling into the pillows on my bed and watching Mom while she amuses herself doing silly human tasks. She's fascinating, always on the move, and rarely, if ever, naps. I don't know where she gets the energy.

I hear a noise in the hallway outside my apartment and watch intently as the man she seems to like approaches our door. I twitch one ear in trepidation. He appears to have something with him and keeps looking down and talking to someone else who must be very short. I wonder who this could be as Mom flings open the door and greets him warmly. Two large, furry beasts rush in with their mouths wide open and teeth exposed. I am immediately alarmed and leap to my feet, preparing for a fight to the death.

But what is this? They're not biting her; they're licking her, and she seems to know these sandy-colored creatures. Fascinating! They flail their long tails and hop around, making quite a racket. I opt to hang back, finding that I have a safe view from my tower that will enable me to pounce on them from above if the need arises. It's best to maintain high ground in a battle.

My ears perk up, and I can feel the hair on my back standing on end as I waffle between curiosity and defensiveness. I think I'm generally a reasonable cat. I don't expect my food to be served out of a golden bowl; I only expect that it is brought to me in a timely manner and combined with water in a precise proportion. I don't complain when Mom gets up at night and disturbs my sleep. I only knock things off the bedside storage box when that guy forgets that he's not allowed to put things there. I always patiently wait for Mom to pour water into the white trough. But this current situation I simply cannot excuse. No one asked my permission or cleared this intrusion with me, yet here we are. I'm assigning blame to all parties involved.

To my dismay, Mom welcomes the beasts, and one suddenly catches sight of me. The other seems completely unaware and busily sniffs around, bumping into Mom and knocking one of the foot coverings with the tempting strings off the rack with its tail. They seem to lack the coordination and grace that I have and must be some inferior subspecies of cats that I've never encountered. They're far larger than any cat I've seen, and their ears are floppy instead of perfect triangles like mine. Perhaps I have discovered a new species.

The one who spotted me has shorter hair and a stockier build. It freezes and stares at me almost timidly, appearing to cower in terror. I puff my chest out a bit, sit up to my full height, and take some satisfaction in this response. Sniffing, I shake my head at their unusual scent, hoping they don't get it on me or any of my stuff. The one who was exploring stops to sniff Mousey, and I am instantly annoyed.

"Excuse me! That's mine! Don't get your stink all over Mousey!" I cry, trying to sound authoritative. I pace in my tower, debating whether to launch myself at the beast.

Mom seems to understand the situation and shoos it away, bringing Mousey over to me and setting him beside my paw. I glance at her, expressing my appreciation with a slow blink, before glaring back at the one cowering by the door and watching me with bulgy eyes. Mom strokes my head and talks to me softly, kissing my cheek and repeating something over and over. Her voice is soothing, and she seems to be at ease, which makes me feel a bit better.

I don't perceive these visitors to be a threat. In fact, one doesn't even appear to know I'm here yet, and the other looks to be frozen in fear. My curiosity begins to take over, and I relax slightly, but not enough to leave the safety of my tower. I sniff again and realize they are both girls. Hmm, this is an interesting development.

Mom tries to coax the scaredy-cat over, and she takes one hesitant step toward me, wagging her tail as Mom talks encouragingly. The man gently guides this beast forward, and she keeps her head down, only occasionally glancing up at me. She appears to be shivering, and I wonder if this is some cold-blooded race or if that is a sign of true terror. I imagine it's intimidating to meet a king. Given my physical prowess and good looks, I can understand why she might be nervous in my presence. Let them cower at my feet.

The other one with the longer hair suddenly looks up, catches sight of me, and ambles over with a goofy smile on her face. She walks right up to the tower and stares at me with her big eyes. She doesn't even bow. Doesn't she know the protocol? I scowl down at her, letting her know exactly who is in charge here.

"Look here," I command. "You shall do as I say, or I shall banish you to the lands beyond that door, where there is no food or water. As my subjects, you will learn not to touch any of my things, and when I say so, you shall sit and wait for me to walk by. Do I make myself clear?"

She doesn't respond and continues to gaze at me and pant heavily, emitting foul breath in my direction. I turn up my nose in disgust and inch backward a few steps. What is the world coming to when others do not practice good hygiene? Did her mother not teach her proper grooming?

The short-haired one continues to just stand there quietly, looking at the floor. She occasionally peers around nervously but doesn't seem interested in exploring. Mom pats her lightly, and she wags her long tail again, looking slightly less miserable. Mom's presence seems to make everyone happy.

77

The man places some food and water bowls down for them. Thank goodness, since I was not about to share mine. I wonder what they are going to use for a litter box because they didn't arrive with one. I hope they don't think they're going to squeeze into mine; that's just too personal for me. There are some things–actually, all things–that I just can't share.

They are wearing similar necklaces to mine, but theirs make a loud jingling sound that is jarring to my ears. How can they ever expect to be mighty hunters with that kind of alarm system tipping off their prey? This seems like a fatal flaw to me. Everyone in the neighborhood will hear them prancing around.

Mom lays out a blanket in the middle of the floor, and they are immediately drawn to it, turning in a circle several times before lying down. I find this behavior curious, and I wonder what they are looking for when they circle around like that. Perhaps this is a trained behavior, or maybe they are fascinated by their own tails and are attempting to get a better look. This thought makes me chuckle. I will spend time considering this later, once I have figured out how to get rid of them.

I don't like that they brought things with them and seem intent on staying a while. They've thrown off my whole day, and now how am I supposed to maintain my regimented nap and snack schedule with these two on the loose? I'll have to pencil in time today for damage control.

Mom crouches down by the intruders, and they look very pleased to be in her presence. She smiles and motions for me to approach, but I just stare back blankly, trying to convince her that no, I don't want to get any closer to these two mouth-breathers who are ruining my home's design scheme with their blanket and bowls strewn about.

She returns to my side and offers words of encouragement and a kiss. She then retreats to the beasts and reaches out to me, like this is really going to change my mind. She repeats this a few times, but I am unwavering and hold my position.

"No," I think. "I'm fine here, but thank you for asking."

She doesn't seem to understand, and this continues until I have to look away and act disinterested to make it stop. My patience is wearing thin just as she finally catches on and leaves me in peace to devise a strategy for evicting these furry intruders.

To their credit, they are lying very still and quiet, and the one did cower before me, which I appreciate. But still, they don't smell right, and they're big and taking up valuable floor space. This is a new problem for me, and I welcome the challenge. I shall emerge victorious and strengthen my claim to this piece of land and all of those who inhabit it.

In order to determine their weaknesses and exploit them, I need to learn more about these new faces. I will observe their ways and formulate a plan. My curiosity returns, and after a few minutes of contemplation, I hop to the ground and slowly advance toward their blanket. They both watch me with interest, and the cowering one barely moves, looking terribly alarmed at my approach, which puts me more at ease. I pause to sniff and am wary of any sudden movements. They just blink harmlessly, and the more adventurous one wags her tail as I draw near. I'm not sure what that means, but she does it while lying down and isn't hissing at me like I would expect one to do before an attack.

I make a half circle around them, never turning my back but trying to signal that I'm not afraid and am in control of the situation, so they had better listen to me and shape up. They watch me intently, and as I approach the cowering one for a closer examination of her tail, she freezes again and looks like she wants to disappear into the floor. With growing confidence, I approach the other one, never getting within biting distance, but getting close enough to assess them.

They don't seem very athletic and look generally a bit lazy. This pleases me, as it confirms that I am the superior animal that is faster, stronger, and braver. Satisfied, I slip into my bedroom, where Mom is observing our interaction. She greets me warmly, and I rub against her legs, looking over my shoulder at the beasts.

"My new subjects can stay for the time being," I declare. "But make sure they don't eat my food or play with my toys, and they certainly are not allowed on my bed."

My New Estate

I have been given a second estate and am touring it for a few days. Mom packed up all of my things, including my favorite toys and canned food, in case the menu at the new place isn't to my liking. While I was nestled in my cozy hideout with the fluffy travel bed, she gently carried me out to a noisy chariot that bumped along, thoroughly shaking me up. I was initially very upset at having been taken out of the house without prior notice and meowed most of the way there. My eyes were wide, and my stomach was unsettled by all the movement. I was hoping we would be there soon and that Mom would stay with me the whole way.

As I knew she would, Mom delivered me safely to my new home away from home. There was a lot of commotion with those beasts I had met before and some unfamiliar people that I'm sure were excited to see me and pledge their loyalty at my earliest convenience. We went into a quiet room with a tall bed that I noted had plenty of room for me to build a fort under. I immediately claimed the bed as mine. Mom opened the door to my hideout, crouched down to peer in, and smiled at me. Her face just makes me so happy, and I know I'm safe when she's by my side. Still, I was initially hesitant to venture out and had to be encouraged. Now that I'm here, there's no use staying tucked away in the confines of my travel bed.

I slink out and quickly assess the room for signs of danger. Nothing looks alarming, so I begin to sniff around, poking my head under the bed, into the closet, and into a bag that was left open, just in case there's anything of interest. You never know what you'll find when you start exploring.

This place smells different. I recognize the beasts' and the man-friend's smells, and I don't mind them, although I do intend to rub up against everything before the day is out and ensure it also smells like me. I grow bolder and stroll about the room before stopping at the closed door. The beasts and the new people are on the other side, and I look at Mom longingly, willing her to open it so I can investigate the rest of this fascinating place.

She does as I command, and the two of us enter a larger room where the beasts are sprawled out on the couch beside the people. I take a hard look at them before timidly moving on. I'm a bit nervous in a new environment, and for a minute I sit underneath a kitchen chair, feeling safe and secure in the confined space. There is so much going on here with the beasts at large and people moving about freely.

I systematically explore every inch of my new domain. I locate my bowl and litter box and am relieved that they made the trip with me. I hop onto what I assume is the table where the people gather for food and have a look around. I love being up high. It's just the best way to get the lay of the land and watch everyone as they go about their business. Most of the time I'm puzzled by it, but I've been watching and judging their actions for years now, and I am rarely amazed by what they do anymore.

Mom continues to hover around me, patting my head and saying things in a pleasant, soft tone. I glance at her lovingly and let out a small meow to let her know I'm paying attention. She bends down, gently touches her forehead to mine, and lets me brush my nose against hers. My heart warms, and I feel increasingly at ease. Mom would never bring me somewhere unsafe.

As the day goes on, I grow more comfortable, wandering about and approaching the beasts from time to time to cautiously sniff them. I find a wonderful perch by a window from which I can comfortably observe people walking outside with their beasts tied to their hands. It seems the beasts lead their people back and forth, up and down this lane where those noisy transportation boxes whiz by. Throughout the day, I begin to notice a pattern. This must be some kind of strange ritual performed in the morning, midday, and at night.

Often, I see the beasts pause here or there and poop out in the open where everyone can see them. Then, as if it were a valuable treasure, their person picks it up and walks away, leaving me to wonder what they intend to do with it once they get home. EWWWW!! Do they just save them all because there is some hidden value I don't comprehend? Note to self: do more research.

I can hear people talking outside, and I see more of those feathered creatures flitting about. They make high-pitched shrieks, and whenever one gets close to where I'm sitting, I watch in awe with a level of concentration I rarely muster for anything else. I could sit here for hours and watch them hop around making those squeaky, shrill noises. They don't appear to have the level of intellect that I possess, but they keep me entertained, so I decide that they are mine as well.

Everyone here worships me, as they should. The beasts give me plenty of room, and one of them still shakes or freezes in my presence. The other people are very kind and are always good for a head scratch. They generally offer some adoring words to make me feel special as I walk by. I like this new estate and plan to spend summers or maybe even winters here in the future.

Over the first few days, I prioritize rubbing against things and proclaiming everything in sight as mine. No one seems to raise any objections, so eventually I just announce, "Let it be known that everything is mine!"

A bit after dinner one night, which was prepared to perfection thanks to Mom's training in the kitchen, I hear a peculiar scratching noise. My ears swivel toward the sound, and I creep forward on silent paws. My eyes grow wide, and I keep low to the ground with my tail twitching slightly, ready to pounce. Something is skittering about under the large metal box used to heat food, and I position myself in front of it, blocking any retreat. I drop my head to the ground, but I can't see anything under there. I settle in to wait. I excel at lying in one spot for long periods in complete silence.

I appear to be in a well-traveled area of the estate, but the humans step over me carefully as they prepare their meals. They stop to watch me occasionally, but I pay them no mind. I'm on a very important mission right now, and I can't be distracted. It's just me and the critter, and I've got nothing to do until breakfast.

I begin to daydream about how I will capture it, pinning it to the floor between my mighty paws or snatching it up by the tail, if it has one. I will trot about, holding up my prize for all to see, and everyone will cheer my name and kiss my head. I shall be called The Great Hunter, and everyone throughout the land will know of my tremendous deed.

The hours pass, and I know it's still under there. Occasionally, I hear its claws scrape the floor, but it doesn't emerge. This is a crafty foe indeed. I assume it must venture out for food and water at some point, and when it does, I'll be here. I am determined to show this newcomer who's the sheriff in this town.

The humans go to their beds, and a while later I realize the critter has been silent for a long time. This seems suspicious to me. I slowly approach the metal box and try to peek underneath again, but I can't make out any distinct shapes. I sit back and ponder the issue. Maybe it has gone to sleep, or perhaps there was a secret passage it used to escape. Perhaps it died of natural causes.

I don't like this, not one bit! But I worry that my time is being wasted waiting for something that has somehow escaped my grasp. After a few minutes of pacing back and forth and debating, I decide to put this task on hold for the night and regroup in the morning.

I trot off to go snuggle with Mom. I need to rest and regain my strength so I'll be ready for round two tomorrow. Believe me, this is far from over.

If I Fits, I Sits

A few times a year, Mom rolls out this box with wheels, fills it full of stuff, and leaves for a few days. I hate when she does this because, despite my always denying her request to leave, she doesn't seem to get the message in time. When she does, I'm sure she turns around and immediately comes back. That's probably why she's never gone for very long.

She pulled the box with wheels out tonight, and I'm melancholy just looking at it. I pace around, trying to decide on the best course of action. She rubs the top of my head, and I purr softly, happy that she's paying attention to me instead of filling the box. I stare at her lovingly, and she whispers something that sounds sweet before kissing my nose.

But then her attention turns back to the box, and I'm slightly annoyed. I shouldn't have to compete for attention with this mere object. It has none of my adorable qualities, and it can't be nearly as interesting as I am. She opens the top, and I immediately jump in, exploring the inside and lying down, satisfied that now she can't put anything in it and must take me wherever it is she goes.

She opens some drawers and begins stacking her colorful fur options on my bed. I watch intently, trying to gauge how much stuff she's taking so I can guess how long she intends to be gone. People seem to need many things to get through their day. I suspect that all of the toys and bowls I would need for an outing could fit in this box, except for my climbing tower and litter box, of course, which would have to travel separately. On second thought, the bed is far too large to fit in here, so I would need a team to transport that for me so my sleep pattern isn't interrupted while away from home.

I stretch out, finding that my front and back paws can only just touch each end of the box if I really reach. If she puts some pillows in here, I think this could be a new bed for the other room, in case I'm too tired to walk all the way to my real bed.

She seems to be tallying up the items she has selected, and I watch with curiosity as she murmurs to herself. If only she spoke feline, then we could chat all day long. Unfortunately, this is not a skill she has learned, and I never know exactly what she's saying either. I have trained her to respond to my body language cues instead, and that system works just fine for us.

Mom looks at me, then at the stacks, then at me, and back at the stacks. She seems unsure for a moment, but then moves the stacks from the bed to the floor beside the box on wheels. Satisfied with this decision, she rubs my cheeks, and I close my eyes happily.

I know when she leaves, some other nice lady will come in to play with me, clean my litter box, and prepare breakfast and dinner, but it's just not the same. Those ladies never know exactly what the preferred food-to-water ratio is, and Mousey's behavior always seems a bit off, although I can't quite put my paw on the reason why. Maybe he's skeptical of them too.

Mom always makes sure I'm taken care of, and I've made some new friends–I mean–new subjects over the years while she's on these little trips. The best part of the trip is when she comes home. I jump into the window every time I hear someone coming down the hall to see if it's her. When it finally is, it's just the best moment ever. I'm so elated to see her and rub eagerly against her legs while she runs her hand over my head and back, again and again. Sometimes she picks me up, and she's so warm and tall that I can see everything from up there. I'm usually not a fan of being carried like this, but when it's a homecoming moment, I want nothing more than to be close to her.

Never Leave Me

Something wonderful has happened, and I can't explain why. I assume it's because I've been wishing extra hard. Mom is suddenly home all day every day, and for days at a time she doesn't leave the house.

Maybe she finally realized that I'm the only thing she needs in life, and she should be home all the time to attend to my every need. Or maybe she has been shunned by the other humans for something, but she's too perfect, and I can't imagine that. Maybe she's done seeing the world, and there's nothing left to explore out there.

I don't understand, but I'm loving every minute of it. Our new schedule consists of breakfast, followed by a long period of sitting at the kitchen table, looking at the bright screen, and tapping away furiously. She sits there most of the day, looking very busy and focused. Occasionally, the smaller glowing rectangle makes an annoying noise, and she talks to someone I can't see.

I don't know what's so important or what this new behavior pattern means, but I try to insert myself into it as much as possible. I wake up from a nap on the couch and listen to the rhythmic tapping. I stretch and wiggle my paws, trying to work out the kinks from lying in the same spot for too long. I watch Mom for a while. She's so focused, and I wonder what she's doing. I hop onto the arm of the couch and launch myself onto the table, skidding to a stop inches from the bright screen. She is startled but looks happy to see me, and I rub my head against her hand, causing the tapping behavior to stop. She gently rubs my cheeks and the itchy spot on my chin. I close my eyes, enjoying the peaceful moment.

But then she turns her attention back to the big glowing device and resumes the tapping. I sit beside her and curl my tail around my feet, looking down at her hands, then up at her face, and then back down at her hands. Does she not see me right here, looking irresistible and demanding attention? I guess I have to be more obvious about what I want. I lower my head and aggressively rub against her hand, making it impossible for her to continue tapping. She pauses again and pats my head gently, but then quickly reverts to her task.

Now I'm starting to get irritated. She doesn't seem to understand me. I pace around the table, then lie down with my tail toward her and stretch my back paws out so they're resting on what I call the "tapping board." The sound stops, and for good measure, I whip my tail back and forth before draping it across the board. She says my name, and my ears swivel toward her excitedly. I must have her full attention now.

She places her hands on my back and gently slides me across the slippery surface until my paws can't reach the board. I sit up and sigh. It's time to regroup and try another tactic. I rise to my paws, approach her again, and nudge her arm until she lifts it, as though to pet me.

Quickly, I drop onto her lap and sit there, looking up at her. She wraps her arms around me and plants kisses on the top of my head. I feel absolutely content and all gooey inside.

When she lets go, I make myself comfortable and curl into a ball, resting my head on her arm, which is supporting my weight. She's so big and strong.

After a while, she repositions me so she can use that arm and goes back to the tapping, but now I have a cozy spot to nap, and there's no way she can forget I'm here. We spend the rest of the afternoon this way, and it is one of the best afternoons I can remember. I can't wait to do this again tomorrow, and the day after that, and the day after that. I hope she never has to leave again.

A Fortress of My Own

Mom brought home a bunch of boxes for me today. They're huge and tall, and unlike the ones that usually show up at the door, they're empty. I sit in the first one she constructed and peer over the top as she organizes the fleet of them around my domain. I'm not sure what brought this on, but I don't question a gift like this when it presents itself.

She begins putting things into another box, and I think, "Hmm, I didn't get the chance to sit in that one."

However, that box looks just like the one I've selected, and I can imagine what sitting in it must be like. Mom moves quickly and deliberately, and soon the box is full. She closes the top and pushes it into a corner of the room, where she scribbles some dark marks on it. It's some kind of coded organization system. I wonder where those items are going or if we're just keeping them safe until they're needed.

She moves on to the next box, loading her colorful human furs in and squishing them down to pile more on top. This intrigues me and requires further investigation. I hop out of my box and amble over for a closer inspection. With a careless leap, I land on top of the stack, enjoying the cushiony feel under my paws. I turn in a circle to thoroughly assess the situation and decide this will do nicely. The box is only about half full, so I feel secure and hidden in here. I can lounge on this soft bedding while Mom continues whatever it is she's doing. Mom kisses my head and whispers to me affectionately before abandoning this box and retrieving another.

We spend the day like this, both of us busy with our tasks. She slowly clears the room of small items and creates an impressive wall of boxes stacked on top of each other, two or three high. It looks like a fortress made for a king like myself. I am pleased with this thought, and after a long afternoon nap, I climb to the highest point of this new tower and gaze out over the rest of the kingdom. I like this vantage point, given I can see all approaching danger, mice, or loyal subjects, and they can see and admire me from afar. Now I understand the point of this exercise. She decided we needed a grand fortress to protect us and let everyone know that I am the ruler of this realm.

The box beside me is not closed, and I lazily paw at one of the flaps on top. It lifts up slightly and flops back down, making a scratching noise that pleases me. I repeat it several times before increasing the speed until I have established a rhythmic beat. I lose myself in the repetition of it for a minute before realizing that Mom is staring at me. I turn toward her and lift my head high, trying to look regal.

"There's nothing to see here," I say quietly, "just making sure the fortress is structurally sound."

She smiles and resumes her manual labor. I admire her unfailing energy and enthusiasm for serving me. It is wonderful to have her around to handle tasks like this.

Meanwhile, the beasts have been sprawled on the floor, watching the proceedings with uncertainty. They look concerned by this new development, and I can't help but feel superior for taking it all in stride. They cannot climb to the top of the tower, and I hold that over them as well. Clearly, this was not designed for them.

Late in the evening, Mom completes the task, and the room is now just furniture and boxes. I was never interested in any of the other things lying about anyway, and she has done a marvelous job cleaning up. Now that all of the surfaces are cleared off, it will be easier for me to jump from one to the other and perch anywhere I please. I don't know why I didn't suggest this sooner.

The Great Journey

Some men arrived today and took the boxes and furniture away, which confused me greatly, as I had only been able to enjoy my new fortress for a few days. But I assume they have relocated them to one of my other residences.

A few things remain, and Mom and the man have been relocating them somewhere for the last hour. I watch curiously and wonder what this new behavior is all about. Once everything is cleared away, Mom humbly presents me with the hideout room that she carries me around in. I eagerly climb aboard and snuggle into the soft bedding. I am anxious to see where we are going and where all the stuff went. I generally don't like leaving my home without prior written notice, but I do like going wherever Mom is, so I have mixed feelings about this.

The beasts come along as well, and we are all taken outside into the chilly air and loaded into one of those noisy transportation boxes. I am situated on some type of pedestal, and the beasts climb in beside me. Mom and the man sit in front of us, and the box begins to move. I look around and can spy some of our stuff piled up behind me. This must be the arranged transportation to my vacation home, or perhaps a new palace altogether. I try to remember if it's my birthday. Maybe this new property is a gift for me. I don't know what day it is, so I decide it could very well be my birthday.

The transportation box sways as it moves, and if I wasn't so intrigued by the trip, it might have lulled me to sleep. I meow a few times, asking about our destination, but they don't understand. It's always worth trying to communicate with them, but they seem to have limited language comprehension skills.

The beasts are lying on the floor in front of and beside me, and they seem excited at the prospect of this new adventure. The one always looks terrified by everything, and she seems particularly nervous today. They smell like they could use a bath, and I turn up my nose to the extent I can in my lounging position.

Eventually, I settle in and feel my eyes grow heavy. I curl up on the soft cushion and am lulled into a peaceful sleep by the swaying. I wake from my nap sometime later and realize we are still on the move. Many hours must have passed, so I now know we are traveling a great distance. Perhaps my mouse forces have conquered some distant land, and we are visiting my new territory to welcome those people into the empire.

At one point, the box stops and the man takes the beasts out, leaving just Mom and me to stare into each other's eyes. She opens the door to my hideout, and I cautiously venture out. I see now that the moving box is indeed packed full of our stuff, and I'm glad to see my cat tower included. I peer out the window and observe an unfamiliar grassy area with other people and their beasts milling about. Many other transportation boxes are situated beside ours, and some have people in them as well. I don't know what to make of this.

Mom tries to get my attention, and I realize she is presenting me with food, water, and my litter box, but I'm not interested right now. There are too many things to look at, and I'm too distracted to think of food or water. She brings the bowls closer, holding them out dutifully. I just look at them, sniff, and then go back to gazing out the window. Eventually, she gives up and puts them away for later.

"I'll let you know when I want them," I think, continuing to watch the other people with growing interest. The world is a fascinating and confusing place.

I hop back into my fuzzy bed, and the beasts return moments later. I consider what I've seen and what this could mean. Perhaps those are all of my newly conquered subjects, but not one of them came up to pet me and bow. It doesn't make sense, but I trust Mom and decide to wait a while longer before making any assumptions.

The moving box continues on its way, and at some point, I doze off again. When I awaken, it's starting to get dark outside, and I realize we must have covered a great distance indeed. I'm starting to get anxious, and I would really like to get wherever we're going so I can walk around and stretch my legs. I've also decided that I'm ready for that food she offered me earlier.

I let out a low meow, and Mom murmurs something gently. I don't know what it means, so I meow again, more forcefully this time. She says something back, but it's not getting me the results I want.

"Stop this box at once, let me out, and begin preparing my dinner!" I command.

She doesn't respond, so I let out a stream of loud and pitiful-sounding meows and wait for her to give in. My annoyance at not being attended to immediately has obviously been disregarded.

Finally, the box stops, and Mom frantically hops out, opens the door nearest me, and snatches up my hideout, hurrying with me toward a building. I am jostled around a bit, but am glad to see some results. She fumbles with the door, and then suddenly I'm looking into an unfamiliar place. The man follows her with the beasts, and Mom gently puts my hideout down to open the gate. I step out skeptically and glance around.

This place doesn't smell like her, and it's certainly new to me. I don't see the box fortress, but perhaps that will be delivered later. I begin to systematically patrol the rooms, and while I am busy doing that, she and the man are quickly bringing in all of my things from the noisy transportation box and stacking them in the first room. It makes an untidy pile, but I am pleased to find that Mom sets my tower by the window and lays out food, water, and my litter box. Just in time too; I have had to pee for a while now!

Once I'm done with my assessment of the new place, I return to the main room, where Mom is sitting quietly, looking exhausted. I rub against her leg, and she obediently pets the top of my head.

"Thanks, Mom, I love my new place!" I coo, knowing I could be happy anywhere as long as we're together.

Daring Explorer

I've been mapping out the new digs inch by inch because I like to know every aspect of my domain. This morning I'm doing my assessment of the food preparation area, casually sniffing while pacing back and forth. It's generally devoid of anything interesting, and I find no signs of wet food. I make a mental note of that. Mom is obviously keeping the open food containers under wraps in that cold box with the tricky handle only she can manage.

I step gingerly into the cold, sunken tray that catches water when it spews out of the hooked nose. It's dry now, but I'm always cautious here because I have found it remains wet long after the water ceases to fall. On more than one occasion, I have gotten my paws damp. I reach the end of the ledge and stare longingly at the cold box with the impossible door problem. I just finished my breakfast, but already I am looking forward to dinner.

I realize the cold box is flat on top, and there is plenty of clearance for me to walk around. I wonder if there is anything of value hidden up there. It would be just like Mom to assume I would never spot something in such a crafty location. I gauge the distance and height for a moment, flex my paws, then line myself up with the center of the box, and crouch into a leaping position.

"And the crowd of adoring fans waves feathers and holds their breath as his majesty prepares to make a mighty leap into the great unknown. Only a cat in prime condition could possibly attempt such a feat of athletic ability. His majesty must be the bravest cat in the land," I announce, feeling every bit the bold and fearless explorer that I am. I really should hire a commentator to follow me around and broadcast the tales of my many adventures.

I check my alignment one last time and spring gracefully from my perch, stretching out to my full length and reaching for the top. My front paws connect with the slippery surface, and my back ones follow, earning me perfect marks for an effortless landing. I take a moment to bask in the achievement.

Then I notice that there is absolutely nothing here. What a disappointment. I had hoped to find a treasure trove of forbidden items stashed away. There is a thin layer of grayish dirt coating the surface, and I realize it is all over my paws. Disgusting. I will have to get one of the minions to clean up this mess, as I will not have filth in my house.

I step lightly across the top, cringing at the thought of having to groom the dirt from my fur and from beneath my expertly sharpened claws. Having to deal with this unsavory task will completely disrupt my morning routine, but sometimes explorers have to get down and dirty for the sake of discovery.

Hmm. I discover that there is a space between the back of the box and the wall, and I approach carefully in case something nefarious is calling that chasm home. I place my front paws at the edge and peer over, only to uncover a small secret room behind the box. I pause for a moment because it too seems empty, but one can never be sure unless one can assess it up close. The space is certainly large enough for me to fit, and it's more a question of how best to descend.

I stretch out one paw and touch the wall, leaning precariously over the edge. There is nothing to hold on to and no ledges halfway down to aim for. I move to one side of the box and carefully assess my options, wondering if I should just hop toward the center and execute a free fall. I place my paws on the back of the box and begin to slide over into the small space behind it, aiming toward the middle. The weight of my front half pulls my back half over, and I position all four feet below me and gracefully arch my back as I descend. I graze the wall for a moment but then land noiselessly, exactly as I had planned.

"Ten points for execution!" I declare, feeling pride well up in my chest.

The space is quite small, but I'm partial to enclosed places. There is a thicker layer of gray dirt here, and it's now swirling around me as I accidentally kicked some of it up upon landing. I'll have to make time for a full spa session after this dirty adventure. It's only a few steps to the wall on one side, and I find I can't quite turn around in here. This is no problem, as I can walk backward and crane my neck around to look at the other side of the space. After a few minutes of this pointless back and forth, I decide that this area has been cleared and there's nothing of interest to be found.

I look up and think for a moment that the lack of ledges is more of an issue on the way back up than it was on the way down. The top of the box now looks impossibly far away, and I can't turn to jump toward it, given the tight fit. I can only face the wall on one side, and that's where I would have to jump. I wonder for a minute if I could run up the wall, then execute a graceful turn once I got high enough, and grab the top of the box. That seems unlikely.

I am quiet for a minute, working through my options and beginning to feel increasingly hopeless. I lean my weight against the box, but it doesn't budge. I'm not going to be able to push it out of the way. I feel the panic and fear set in, and I suddenly wish I hadn't decided to explore this space.

"Mom! Mom, help!" I cry pitifully, just wanting her to hold me and put me back in the soft bed, where I should have stayed. "Mom! Help! Help!"

I hear her footsteps moving around, and she calls my name softly. She moves from room to room, but she passes by the box without pausing.

"Mom! I'm here! I'm here!" I squeal, my terror rising. "I'm trapped; help me get out of here! Get the servants and the mouse army to help!"

She passes by again but seems to be honing in on this area. Now she's pacing back and forth, presumably searching for me, but never thinking to look here.

"Behind the box!" I yell. "Look behind the cold box!"

I hear the door of the cold box open and close, and she pauses for a moment. Then I hear some shuffling, and the cold box shifts forward a tiny bit.

"That's it! I'm here! Tell my subjects to get me out of here at once!" I command.

Her footsteps retreat to the bedroom, and I hear her talking to the man for a minute. Then two sets of footsteps return, and there is some muffled grumbling. The box begins to move again and is slowly pulled forward until it clears the wall on one side, creating an opening large enough to slip through. I casually stroll out, not wanting everyone to know that I was afraid. A ruler must never show fear.

"Good boy!" I say to the man over my shoulder.

I rub against Mom's legs a few times and then wander off to start the grooming process. Everything is worth trying once, but I don't think I'll be going back to that secret room again.

Secret Messages

Now that the man officially lives with us in our new place, I have obviously claimed all of his worldly belongings as my own. I consider them gifts or tributes in honor of my reign.

I particularly like that he has a rather large platform that mysteriously rises up and down with a whirring sound and provides a great lookout point for me. He has one of those big bright rectangles on it and a flat board that he taps away on all day. I'm never sure what to make of this behavior, and I assume it must be some primitive form of communication or entertainment based on a series of taps. But no one ever taps back to him, so I conclude he must not be very popular, or else he's just talking to himself.

He stares intently at the screen sometimes, one hand positioned on a small object that emits clicking sounds when he slides it around the platform. I like to observe him from the comfy bed in the room and try to better understand his habits. I always attempt to relate to my loyal subjects. Given he can open cans of food, I have learned to enjoy our friendship.

The man walks out of the room, I presume to take his midday snack break, and I debate following him or going back to sleep. But then a genius idea dawns on me.

Excitedly, I trot to the edge of the bed, assess the distance, test my back legs, and then leap through the air like a winged god and land gracefully beside the tapping board, only knocking one paper onto the floor. He can pick that up later.

The screen is still bright, and there are a lot of squares and lines on it that I don't understand. I approach the tapping board and sniff it to check for booby traps and other dangers. It doesn't really smell like anything— maybe something artificial. I position myself in front of it, like he does, and look from it to the screen, mimicking his motions. Then I look at the small object that he slides around, and I wonder how all of these things interact to communicate with others. They don't look like fun toys. They're all black and not fluffy with feathers or anything, so I decide it must be communication-related.

If humans can make this thing work, then given my superior intellect, I'm certain I can figure it out too. I wonder how to start my message. Reaching out with my front paw, I tap the board several times, being rewarded with the characteristic sound. I think hard about what to say.

Life by Pumpkin: A Cat's View on Everything

Dear Fish Suppliers:

As your lord and commander, I demand that you swiftly send your best salmon and tuna for dinner tonight. I will accept only the freshest and most tasty of your inventory, and anything less will be considered treason. Do ensure that there are no peas or carrots in them, as I hate when plants are included in my food.

I am wintering at my new residence, and you can contact Mom for the details, as she is also the one who will be preparing my meals.

King Pumpkin

I sit back and swat the object that glides around for good measure. I hope this ensures that the message was sent to the right place. My tail is hanging off the edge of the platform, and I flick it back and forth gently, feeling incredibly pleased with myself. I don't know why I never thought of doing this sooner. Going forward, this will allow me to communicate with my subjects both near and far without ever having to leave the comfort of my home.

Then I wonder if I should have sent the message to the fish telling them where to go tonight. Hmm, I don't know how this process works. Do the fish transport themselves here, or does someone deliver them? I start a new message just to be safe.

To the Fish of My Realm:

I require the services of local salmon and tuna for tonight's dinner and want only the healthiest of you, so I can maintain my strength. You must arrive no later than sundown, as I do not like my dinner to be delayed, and we must allow for prep time. Going forward, I would like one of each of you to arrive daily at the allotted time.

You may make yourself known to my mother when you arrive, and she will ensure you are taken care of and compensated for your time and efforts.

King Pumpkin

I hit the moving object again, and it slides close to the edge of the platform but doesn't fall off. I stare at it for a moment, wondering if I should push it onto the floor, but I decide not to in case there's another message I need to send.

I hear footsteps approaching and swiftly leap back to the bed. I stretch out lazily, as though I have been here the whole time. Only one other piece of paper flutters to the ground.

When the man returns, he pauses, picks up the papers, looks at me, looks at the platform, and then back at me. I just gaze out the window and pretend like he is completely uninteresting. He sits back down, resumes tapping away, and I drift off for my afternoon nap after a hard day of work and dream about my imminent fish delivery.

Leslie Popp

The Best Day of the Year

The most magical time of the year is when Mom wraps a bunch of boxes in crinkly paper, tops them with shiny ribbons, and stacks them on the ground for me to inspect and sometimes remove the ribbons if I decide to play with them. Everyone always seems so excited during this time of year. Then one day, Mom, the man, and whoever else happens to be around engage in a fascinating ritual of removing the ribbons and paper, tossing them on the floor, extracting whatever is in the boxes in wonder, and then casting the boxes aside.

Their interest seems to be completely misplaced, and they take no interest in sitting in the boxes, chasing the ribbon across the wood floor, or hiding under the paper. It is a treasure trove of toys, and I am almost overwhelmed deciding what to play with first every year.

A few days ago, the process began with Mom covering the boxes in the crinkly paper and arranging the ribbons. I helped, of course, with the quality control and oversaw the process from start to finish. They are now perched in a neat stack on top of a central table. I have been waiting impatiently for the moment when the opening process begins, and each day I get more and more anxious.

Life by Pumpkin: A Cat's View on Everything

This morning some unfamiliar people arrived, and instinct tells me that today is the day. Everyone seems cheerful, and there has been much commotion, which is interfering with my normal nap schedule. The excitement is rubbing off on me, and the anticipation of the toys to come has given me super cat energy.

I sit calmly on the edge of Mom's desk, where her tapping board resides, my tail flicking casually as I observe the proceedings. I try to look uninterested, but make no mistake, I am single-mindedly watching for signs of box opening time. Soon I am rewarded for my diligence, and everyone takes a seat around the boxes and begins handing them around.

I don't know how they select who opens what. Perhaps it is by color or smell, or in order from youngest to oldest. There does seem to be some system, but I haven't yet cracked that code. They all appear so pleased, and there is constant chatter. I shift from paw to paw as the first ribbon is removed, and I watch greedily as it is tossed to the ground.

I spring to the floor and stalk over to it, whacking it with one paw and sending it skittering away with a satisfying scraping sound. I give chase, but then realize the crinkly paper is now raining down and creating a pile beside the central stack of boxes. I pause, unsure of what to do. I give the ribbon one more swat for good measure, then race back and slide headfirst into the paper with a pleasing crunch. I lie down, flattening it beneath me. Then I paw at an edge sticking up, and it makes a delightful rustling sound. I bite that edge, just to show it who's boss.

But now I see a different type of ribbon has been unraveled by someone on the other side of the crowd, and it is still attached to its piece of flimsy paper. I rush over to inspect it, take a bite, and then spit it out in disgust. I always forget that it never tastes very appealing. I drag it out from under the table with the boxes and deposit it a few feet away. I proceed to paw at the ribbon, then the paper, then the ribbon again. I am determined to separate the two.

Again, I am distracted from my task when an empty box hits the ground. I spring over and fling myself into it, thereby claiming it for myself. It is a bit small, but every box counts, and I want to make sure I claim them all so I don't miss out on any. How are you supposed to figure out which one is best if you don't try all of them? Feeling extremely pleased, I sit in the box, inspecting the edges and deciding that it is very sturdy, although too small to lie in. Luckily, another box comes up for grabs moments later.

"MINE! MINE!" I cry, scurrying over to test that one out as well. It's much larger, with high sides that I have to hop over, and I decide it would make an excellent clubhouse to hide in with Mousey or Ms. Fish. I turn in a circle to inspect my prize, and as I do, Mom places one of the ribbons in it. I quickly hunker down with both paws on top of the ribbon, almost overcome with joy. This is just the best day ever.

Life by Pumpkin: A Cat's View on Everything

I look up at Mom and realize she is smiling down affectionately, her love for me shining in her eyes. I am so grateful for her, and I try to communicate, with a slow blink and a small noise, just how much I love her too.

The commotion continues for a while, and I manage to claim every box, ribbon, and crinkly paper in sight. Overall, it has been a beautiful day, but now I'm tuckered out. The other people finally leave, and it's blissfully quiet again.

I feel comfortable leaving my stash of presents for a while and wandering into the bedroom to get some much-needed rest. The man is sprawled out on the bed, and I hop up next to him, sniffing his arm for a moment and watching him curiously. He is breathing softly and looks so peaceful.

Noiselessly, I march up to him and curl up in the space between his arm and his side, where I can be snug and warm. I drape my paws across his arm and rest my head on them, sighing contentedly. I drift off into a deep sleep, thinking about how lucky I am to be so loved.

Leslie Popp

Author's Bio

Leslie Popp is the author of the *Life by Pumpkin* series. Her affinity for writing was ingrained from an early age, starting with elementary school Write-A-Book contests, which she treated as a serious literary pursuit. She works in finance but loves to write about her furry companions, among other subjects. Leslie has always harbored a deep love of animals, and her pets over the years have included hermit crabs, guinea pigs, cats, and dogs. She adheres to the belief that pets are members of the family and deserve respect, love, and sometimes their own pillow on the bed. She firmly supports the humane treatment of all animals and is committed to a vegan lifestyle.

Leslie Popp

Pumpkin's Bio

Pumpkin (2007–2021) was an orange tabby with a loving heart and a big personality. He adopted Leslie in 2010 after meeting her at the animal shelter where she volunteered. Pumpkin had been housed there for a year, and he was overjoyed to find his perfect human and forever home. His curiosity and desire for attention resulted in his many chronicled adventures. Pumpkin did indeed have his own pillow and side of the bed, as well as a dedicated coffee mug for water in case the water in his bowl was not to his liking that day. He brought joy to all those around him and will always be missed.

Synopsis

Life by Pumpkin: A Cat's View on Everything chronicles the heartwarming adventures of Pumpkin, an orange tabby with determined curiosity, a desire for undivided attention, and dreams of world dominance. He provides instruction on how to train your human and an analysis of their odd rituals, such as standing under falling water in the morning, changing their fur daily, and being obsessed with portable, lighted rectangles that periodically make annoying noises. Pumpkin offers his views on everything, including how to handle intruders, the importance of morning yoga, and the best day of the year when boxes, ribbons, and crinkly paper are strewn about the floor in abundance. Pumpkin provides a glimpse of the world through a cat's eyes and isn't afraid to tell us what he thinks.

Leslie Popp

Quotes and Reviews

"I am a god among men, master of my domain, and ruler of the free world! I reign over every inch of this apartment, and my army of loyal mouse toys is at my disposal. I leave no corner unexplored, no box unturned, and no high ledge unexamined, no matter the potential danger. I nap whenever and wherever I please, but mostly I prefer fuzzy blankets, the sunny spot by the window, or the cradle of my climbing tower, with my blue and white fish toy tucked under my chin."

 - Pumpkin

"This true story is a delightfully captivating tale about the greatest cat that ever lived. My mom does an excellent job capturing and documenting my thoughts and memorable reign in a book that is long overdue."

- Pumpkin

Made in the USA
Columbia, SC
26 September 2024